Table of Contents

D1385342

How to Use This Book

This Premium Education Series workbook is designed to suit your teaching needs. Since every child learns at his or her own pace, this workbook can be used individually or as part of small group instruction. The activity pages can be used together with other educational materials and are easily applied to a variety of teaching approaches.

Contents

A detailed table of contents lists all the skills that are covered in the workbook.

Units

The workbook is divided into units of related skills. Numbered tabs allow you to quickly locate each unit. The skills within each unit are designed to be progressively more challenging.

Activity Pages

Each activity page is titled with the skill being practiced or reinforced. The activities and units in this workbook can be used in sequential order, or they can be used to accommodate and supplement any educational curriculum. In addition, the activity pages include simple instructions to encourage independent study, and they are printed in black and white so they can be easily reproduced. Plus, you can record the child's name and the date the activity was completed on each page to keep track of learning progress.

Practice Test

A comprehensive practice test helps prepare the child for standardized testing in a stress-free environment. Presented in the fill-in-the-circle format, this test includes skills covered on standardized tests.

Answer Key

The pages in the back of the workbook provide answers for each activity page as well as the practice test. These answer pages allow you to quickly check the child's work and provide immediate feedback on how he or she is progressing.

Addition Facts to 18

Name_____ Date_____

$$\begin{array}{r} 10 \\ +\ 8 \\ \hline 18 \end{array}$$

Add.

1.
$$\begin{array}{r} 9 \\ +\ 8 \\ \hline \end{array}$$
$$\begin{array}{r} 7 \\ +\ 4 \\ \hline \end{array}$$
$$\begin{array}{r} 9 \\ +\ 9 \\ \hline \end{array}$$
$$\begin{array}{r} 6 \\ +\ 8 \\ \hline \end{array}$$
$$\begin{array}{r} 6 \\ +\ 6 \\ \hline \end{array}$$

2.
$$\begin{array}{r} 6 \\ +\ 9 \\ \hline \end{array}$$
$$\begin{array}{r} 7 \\ +\ 6 \\ \hline \end{array}$$
$$\begin{array}{r} 9 \\ +\ 5 \\ \hline \end{array}$$
$$\begin{array}{r} 8 \\ +\ 8 \\ \hline \end{array}$$
$$\begin{array}{r} 4 \\ +\ 5 \\ \hline \end{array}$$

3.
$$\begin{array}{r} 6 \\ +\ 3 \\ \hline \end{array}$$
$$\begin{array}{r} 8 \\ +\ 7 \\ \hline \end{array}$$
$$\begin{array}{r} 9 \\ +\ 2 \\ \hline \end{array}$$
$$\begin{array}{r} 8 \\ +\ 1 \\ \hline \end{array}$$
$$\begin{array}{r} 7 \\ +\ 3 \\ \hline \end{array}$$

4.
$$\begin{array}{r} 5 \\ +\ 5 \\ \hline \end{array}$$
$$\begin{array}{r} 8 \\ +\ 4 \\ \hline \end{array}$$
$$\begin{array}{r} 9 \\ +\ 7 \\ \hline \end{array}$$
$$\begin{array}{r} 7 \\ +\ 7 \\ \hline \end{array}$$
$$\begin{array}{r} 6 \\ +\ 5 \\ \hline \end{array}$$

Addition Terms

Name_____ Date_____

Addends are the numbers added together to form a sum.

→ addend ←

Write the missing **addends**.

1.
$$\begin{array}{r} 6 \\ + \\ \hline 13 \end{array} \quad \begin{array}{r} 8 \\ + \\ \hline 16 \end{array} \quad \begin{array}{r} \\ +\ 7 \\ \hline 12 \end{array} \quad \begin{array}{r} \\ +\ 8 \\ \hline 10 \end{array} \quad \begin{array}{r} 9 \\ + \\ \hline 17 \end{array}$$

2.
$$\begin{array}{r} \\ +\ 5 \\ \hline 11 \end{array} \quad \begin{array}{r} \\ +\ 7 \\ \hline 14 \end{array} \quad \begin{array}{r} 9 \\ + \\ \hline 18 \end{array} \quad \begin{array}{r} 8 \\ + \\ \hline 12 \end{array} \quad \begin{array}{r} \\ +\ 4 \\ \hline 9 \end{array}$$

3.
$$\begin{array}{r} 7 \\ + \\ \hline 16 \end{array} \quad \begin{array}{r} \\ +\ 9 \\ \hline 11 \end{array} \quad \begin{array}{r} \\ +\ 8 \\ \hline 13 \end{array} \quad \begin{array}{r} 5 \\ + \\ \hline 8 \end{array} \quad \begin{array}{r} \\ +\ 9 \\ \hline 15 \end{array}$$

Subtraction Facts to 18

Name_____ Date_____

$$\begin{array}{r} 10 \\ -\ 5 \\ \hline 5 \end{array}$$

Subtract.

1.
$$\begin{array}{r} 10 \\ -\ 7 \\ \hline \end{array}$$
$$\begin{array}{r} 12 \\ -\ 6 \\ \hline \end{array}$$
$$\begin{array}{r} 18 \\ -\ 9 \\ \hline \end{array}$$
$$\begin{array}{r} 16 \\ -\ 7 \\ \hline \end{array}$$
$$\begin{array}{r} 12 \\ -\ 8 \\ \hline \end{array}$$

2.
$$\begin{array}{r} 15 \\ -\ 7 \\ \hline \end{array}$$
$$\begin{array}{r} 13 \\ -\ 9 \\ \hline \end{array}$$
$$\begin{array}{r} 17 \\ -\ 8 \\ \hline \end{array}$$
$$\begin{array}{r} 11 \\ -\ 8 \\ \hline \end{array}$$
$$\begin{array}{r} 14 \\ -\ 6 \\ \hline \end{array}$$

3.
$$\begin{array}{r} 13 \\ -\ 5 \\ \hline \end{array}$$
$$\begin{array}{r} 11 \\ -\ 6 \\ \hline \end{array}$$
$$\begin{array}{r} 15 \\ -\ 8 \\ \hline \end{array}$$
$$\begin{array}{r} 16 \\ -\ 9 \\ \hline \end{array}$$
$$\begin{array}{r} 11 \\ -\ 2 \\ \hline \end{array}$$

4.
$$\begin{array}{r} 13 \\ -\ 7 \\ \hline \end{array}$$
$$\begin{array}{r} 15 \\ -\ 9 \\ \hline \end{array}$$
$$\begin{array}{r} 17 \\ -\ 9 \\ \hline \end{array}$$
$$\begin{array}{r} 16 \\ -\ 8 \\ \hline \end{array}$$
$$\begin{array}{r} 12 \\ -\ 7 \\ \hline \end{array}$$

Subtraction Terms

Name_____ Date_____

The **subtrahend** is the number subtracted from another number to find the difference.

$$10 - 6 = 4$$

↑
subtrahend

Write the missing **subtrahends**.

1.

17	11	16	7	18
−	−	−	−	−
9	7	8	2	9

2.

14	15	13	9	12
−	−	−	−	−
8	7	4	6	5

3.

11	14	10	16	15
−	−	−	−	−
5	7	6	7	9

Review Facts to 18

Name_____ Date_____

Fill in the circle next to the correct answer.

1.
$$\begin{array}{r} 5 \\ +\ 8 \\ \hline \end{array}$$
○ a) 12
○ b) 13
○ c) 14

2.
$$\begin{array}{r} 9 \\ -\ 5 \\ \hline \end{array}$$
○ a) 4
○ b) 10
○ c) 14

3.
$$\begin{array}{r} 8 \\ +\ 8 \\ \hline \end{array}$$
○ a) 0
○ b) 8
○ c) 16

4.
$$\begin{array}{r} 9 \\ +\ 5 \\ \hline \end{array}$$
○ a) 4
○ b) 10
○ c) 14

5.
$$\begin{array}{r} 17 \\ -\ 9 \\ \hline \end{array}$$
○ a) 7
○ b) 8
○ c) 9

6.
$$\begin{array}{r} 10 \\ -\ 3 \\ \hline \end{array}$$
○ a) 7
○ b) 8
○ c) 9

7.
$$\begin{array}{r} 4 \\ +\ 7 \\ \hline \end{array}$$
○ a) 9
○ b) 10
○ c) 11

8.
$$\begin{array}{r} 15 \\ -\ 8 \\ \hline \end{array}$$
○ a) 6
○ b) 7
○ c) 8

9.
$$\begin{array}{r} 6 \\ +\ 4 \\ \hline \end{array}$$
○ a) 2
○ b) 9
○ c) 10

10.
$$\begin{array}{r} 18 \\ -\ 9 \\ \hline \end{array}$$
○ a) 9
○ b) 8
○ c) 7

11.
$$\begin{array}{r} 8 \\ +\ 6 \\ \hline \end{array}$$
○ a) 2
○ b) 14
○ c) 15

12.
$$\begin{array}{r} 13 \\ -\ 5 \\ \hline \end{array}$$
○ a) 8
○ b) 9
○ c) 10

13.
$$\begin{array}{r} 7 \\ +\ 9 \\ \hline \end{array}$$
○ a) 15
○ b) 16
○ c) 17

14.
$$\begin{array}{r} 12 \\ -\ 6 \\ \hline \end{array}$$
○ a) 6
○ b) 8
○ c) 18

15.
$$\begin{array}{r} 6 \\ +\ 5 \\ \hline \end{array}$$
○ a) 1
○ b) 11
○ c) 13

Fact Families

Name_____ Date_____

A **fact family** consists of two addition and two subtraction problems using the same three numbers.

The fact family for 4, 5, and 9 is:

$$4 + 5 = 9 \qquad 9 - 4 = 5$$

$$5 + 4 = 9 \qquad 9 - 5 = 4$$

Complete each fact family.

1.

$\square + 7 = 10$

$7 + \square = 10$

$10 - \square = 7$

$10 - 7 = \square$

2.

$6 + \square = 13$

$\square + 6 = 13$

$13 - 6 = \square$

$13 - \square = 6$

3.

$\square + 8 = 12$

$8 + \square = 12$

$12 - \square = 8$

$12 - 8 = \square$

4.

$5 + \square = 14$

$\square + 5 = 14$

$14 - 5 = \square$

$14 - \square = 5$

5.

$\square + 9 = 11$

$9 + \square = 11$

$11 - \square = 9$

$11 - 9 = \square$

6.

$7 + \square = 15$

$\square + 7 = 15$

$15 - 7 = \square$

$15 - \square = 7$

7.

$\square + 6 = 11$

$6 + \square = 11$

$11 - \square = 6$

$11 - 6 = \square$

8.

$8 + \square = 9$

$\square + 8 = 9$

$9 - 8 = \square$

$9 - \square = 8$

9.

$\square + 9 = 17$

$9 + \square = 17$

$17 - \square = 9$

$17 - 9 = \square$

Name_____ Date_____

Write the missing symbol.

 **or**

1. 5 ☐ 3 = 8   4 ☐ 1 = 3   9 ☐ 4 = 5

2. 7 ☐ 2 = 5   3 ☐ 3 = 6   3 ☐ 2 = 1

3. 1 ☐ 6 = 7   4 ☐ 4 = 0   8 ☐ 6 = 2

4. 12 ☐ 5 = 7   9 ☐ 2 = 11   18 ☐ 9 = 9

5. 8 ☐ 6 = 14   13 ☐ 4 = 9   16 ☐ 8 = 8

6. 8 ☐ 9 = 17   5 ☐ 3 = 2   8 ☐ 1 = 9

7. 10 ☐ 5 = 5   15 ☐ 8 = 7   6 ☐ 6 = 12

8. 14 ☐ 2 = 16   4 ☐ 8 = 12   11 ☐ 5 = 6

9. 9 ☐ 3 = 12   17 ☐ 6 = 11   8 ☐ 2 = 10

Two-Digit Addition

First add the ones. Then add the tens.

tens	ones
3	4
+ 5	3
8	7

Add.

1.
```
  12        16        62        32        47
+ 27      + 42      + 21      + 43      + 30
```

2.
```
  35        17        10        11        23
+ 14      + 11      + 61      + 44      + 46
```

3.
```
  26        18        42        22        65
+ 22      + 80      + 42      + 16      + 21
```

4.
```
  22        30        53        67        42
+ 51      + 62      + 15      + 20      + 32
```

Two-Digit Subtraction

Name_____ Date_____

First subtract the ones. Then subtract the tens.

tens	ones
5	6
− 2	5
3	1

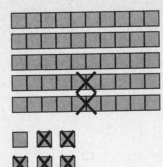

Subtract.

1.
59 98 40 89 47
− 22 − 75 − 10 − 65 − 30

2.
77 82 29 32 63
− 66 − 51 − 17 − 10 − 42

3.
39 90 64 59 67
− 14 − 50 − 51 − 43 − 21

4.
74 88 69 57 45
− 21 − 44 − 22 − 42 − 32

Checking Subtraction

Name _____ Date _____

Subtract. Then add to check.

1.
$$\begin{array}{r} 66 \\ -\ 24 \\ \hline 42 \end{array} \qquad \begin{array}{r} 42 \\ +\ 24 \\ \hline 66 \end{array}$$

2.
$$\begin{array}{r} 83 \\ -\ 52 \\ \hline \square \end{array} \qquad \begin{array}{r} \square \\ +\ 52 \\ \hline 83 \end{array}$$

3.
$$\begin{array}{r} 46 \\ -\ 26 \\ \hline \square \end{array} \qquad \begin{array}{r} \square \\ +\ 26 \\ \hline 46 \end{array}$$

4.
$$\begin{array}{r} 52 \\ -\ 41 \\ \hline \square \end{array} \qquad \begin{array}{r} \square \\ +\ 41 \\ \hline 52 \end{array}$$

5.
$$\begin{array}{r} 79 \\ -\ 17 \\ \hline \square \end{array} \qquad \begin{array}{r} \square \\ +\ 17 \\ \hline 79 \end{array}$$

6.
$$\begin{array}{r} 96 \\ -\ 61 \\ \hline \square \end{array} \qquad \begin{array}{r} \square \\ +\ 61 \\ \hline 96 \end{array}$$

7.
$$\begin{array}{r} 45 \\ -\ 33 \\ \hline \square \end{array} \qquad \begin{array}{r} \square \\ +\ 33 \\ \hline 45 \end{array}$$

8.
$$\begin{array}{r} 97 \\ -\ 21 \\ \hline \square \end{array} \qquad \begin{array}{r} \square \\ +\ 21 \\ \hline 97 \end{array}$$

9.
$$\begin{array}{r} 67 \\ -\ 50 \\ \hline \square \end{array} \qquad \begin{array}{r} \square \\ +\ 50 \\ \hline 67 \end{array}$$

10.
$$\begin{array}{r} 99 \\ -\ 45 \\ \hline \square \end{array} \qquad \begin{array}{r} \square \\ +\ 45 \\ \hline 99 \end{array}$$

11.
$$\begin{array}{r} 78 \\ -\ 34 \\ \hline \square \end{array} \qquad \begin{array}{r} \square \\ +\ 34 \\ \hline 78 \end{array}$$

12.
$$\begin{array}{r} 35 \\ -\ 12 \\ \hline \square \end{array} \qquad \begin{array}{r} \square \\ +\ 12 \\ \hline 35 \end{array}$$

Two-Digit Practice

Name_____ Date_____

Fill in the circle next to the correct answer.

1.
$$\begin{array}{r} 56 \\ + \ 41 \\ \hline \end{array}$$
○ a) 15
○ b) 85
○ c) 97

2.
$$\begin{array}{r} 95 \\ - \ 53 \\ \hline \end{array}$$
○ a) 42
○ b) 48
○ c) 84

3.
$$\begin{array}{r} 81 \\ + \ 18 \\ \hline \end{array}$$
○ a) 89
○ b) 98
○ c) 99

4.
$$\begin{array}{r} 39 \\ + \ 50 \\ \hline \end{array}$$
○ a) 29
○ b) 89
○ c) 99

5.
$$\begin{array}{r} 67 \\ - \ 42 \\ \hline \end{array}$$
○ a) 25
○ b) 26
○ c) 29

6.
$$\begin{array}{r} 70 \\ - \ 30 \\ \hline \end{array}$$
○ a) 20
○ b) 40
○ c) 90

7.
$$\begin{array}{r} 46 \\ + \ 23 \\ \hline \end{array}$$
○ a) 23
○ b) 63
○ c) 69

8.
$$\begin{array}{r} 75 \\ - \ 25 \\ \hline \end{array}$$
○ a) 50
○ b) 60
○ c) 70

9.
$$\begin{array}{r} 64 \\ + \ 34 \\ \hline \end{array}$$
○ a) 88
○ b) 98
○ c) 99

10.
$$\begin{array}{r} 88 \\ - \ 44 \\ \hline \end{array}$$
○ a) 22
○ b) 44
○ c) 66

11.
$$\begin{array}{r} 18 \\ + \ 11 \\ \hline \end{array}$$
○ a) 29
○ b) 28
○ c) 27

12.
$$\begin{array}{r} 53 \\ - \ 32 \\ \hline \end{array}$$
○ a) 20
○ b) 21
○ c) 22

13.
$$\begin{array}{r} 73 \\ + \ 12 \\ \hline \end{array}$$
○ a) 61
○ b) 81
○ c) 85

14.
$$\begin{array}{r} 92 \\ - \ 60 \\ \hline \end{array}$$
○ a) 30
○ b) 32
○ c) 42

15.
$$\begin{array}{r} 51 \\ + \ 25 \\ \hline \end{array}$$
○ a) 76
○ b) 67
○ c) 36

Word Problems: Addition (1)

Name _____ Date _____

Read each problem. Write a number sentence and solve.

1. 12 cats are at the pet parade. Then 17 more cats join the parade. How many cats are in the parade now?

$$\begin{array}{r} 12 \\ +\ 17 \\ \hline 29 \end{array}$$

2. 26 dogs are in the park. 11 more dogs come. How many dogs are in the park now?

_____

3. Serina has 45 goldfish in her tank. Ray has 32 goldfish in his tank. How many goldfish are in both tanks?

_____

4. Jeff had 50 guppies. His mother bought him 18 more guppies. How many guppies will Jeff have now?

_____

5. 16 horses are in the barn. 10 more horses are brought in the barn. How many horses are in the barn now?

6. 34 cows are grazing in the grass. Then 24 more cows come along. How many cows are there now?

_____

Name_____ Date_____

Read each problem. Write a number sentence and solve.

1. Farmer Bob had 24 tomato plants in the garden. He removed 11 of them. How many tomato plants are left?

$$\begin{array}{r} 24 \\ -11 \\ \hline 13 \end{array}$$

2. Jamie had 56 carrots. She put 25 of them in her stew. How many carrots does she have left?

_____

3. Marlene had 49 heads of lettuce in her garden. A rabbit ate 21 of them. How many heads of lettuce are left?

_____

4. Joseph had 88 apples on his tree. 42 of them fell off. How many apples are left on the tree?

_____

5. Ben planted 27 cucumber plants in his garden. He gave 16 of them away. How many plants are left in the garden?

_____

6. Julie saw 77 pears on the tree. She picked 54 of them. How many pears were left on the tree?

_____

Name_____ Date_____

Read each problem. Write a number sentence and solve.

1. Eddie had 89 pieces of candy. He gave 26 of them to Preston. How many pieces of candy does Eddie have left?

_____

2. Jennifer had 42 stamps. Her mom gave her 36 more. How many stamps does Jennifer have now?

_____

3. Bobby had 95 marbles. He lost 45 of them. How many marbles does Bobby have left?

_____

4. David had 53 cars. He gave 12 of them to his brother. How many cars does David have left?

_____

5. Erica has 61 dolls. Heather has 38 dolls. How many dolls do they have altogether?

_____

6. Karen had 24 beads. Linda gave her 13 more. How many beads does Karen have now?

_____

Adding Three Numbers

Name_____ Date_____

Add.

1.
   40   10   61   56   13
   20   26   27   20   12
 + 30   + 31   + 10   + 10   + 11

2.
   20   23   30   14   10
   22   61   12   43   22
 + 24   + 15   + 13   + 20   + 11

3.
   16   21   14   26   30
   21   32   13   21   30
 + 50   + 23   + 22   + 11   + 30

4.
   18   20   20   41   52
   10   34   16   27   12
 + 11   + 14   + 23   + 20   + 10

Subtracting More Than Once

Name_____ Date_____

Subtract.

1.
```
   54
 - 13
 ┌────┐
 │ 41 │
 └────┘
 - 20
 ┌────┐
 │ 21 │
 └────┘
 - 11
 ┌────┐
 │ 10 │
 └────┘
```

2.
```
   67
 - 22
 ┌────┐
 │    │
 └────┘
 - 25
 ┌────┐
 │    │
 └────┘
 - 10
 ┌────┐
 │    │
 └────┘
```

3.
```
   23
 - 13
 ┌────┐
 │    │
 └────┘
 -  6
 ┌────┐
 │    │
 └────┘
 -  3
 ┌────┐
 │    │
 └────┘
```

4.
```
   48
 - 17
 ┌────┐
 │    │
 └────┘
 - 20
 ┌────┐
 │    │
 └────┘
 -  7
 ┌────┐
 │    │
 └────┘
```

5.
```
   39
 - 10
 ┌────┐
 │    │
 └────┘
 -  7
 ┌────┐
 │    │
 └────┘
 - 11
 ┌────┐
 │    │
 └────┘
```

6.
```
   88
 - 24
 ┌────┐
 │    │
 └────┘
 - 30
 ┌────┐
 │    │
 └────┘
 - 12
 ┌────┐
 │    │
 └────┘
 - 20
 ┌────┐
 │    │
 └────┘
```

7.
```
   72
 - 31
 ┌────┐
 │    │
 └────┘
 - 20
 ┌────┐
 │    │
 └────┘
 - 11
 ┌────┐
 │    │
 └────┘
 -  6
 ┌────┐
 │    │
 └────┘
```

8.
```
   99
 - 35
 ┌────┐
 │    │
 └────┘
 - 13
 ┌────┐
 │    │
 └────┘
 - 20
 ┌────┐
 │    │
 └────┘
 - 21
 ┌────┐
 │    │
 └────┘
```

9.
```
   57
 - 10
 ┌────┐
 │    │
 └────┘
 - 15
 ┌────┐
 │    │
 └────┘
 - 10
 ┌────┐
 │    │
 └────┘
 - 22
 ┌────┐
 │    │
 └────┘
```

10.
```
   64
 - 13
 ┌────┐
 │    │
 └────┘
 - 31
 ┌────┐
 │    │
 └────┘
 - 10
 ┌────┐
 │    │
 └────┘
 -  7
 ┌────┐
 │    │
 └────┘
```

Name_____ Date_____

Unit 1

tens	ones
2	7
+ 3	5

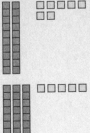

Add the ones.
7 ones + 5 ones =
12 ones

tens	ones
1	
2	7
+ 3	5
	2

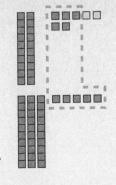

Regroup 12 ones as
1 ten and 2 ones.

tens	ones
1	
2	7
+ 3	5
6	2

Add the tens.
1 ten + 2 tens + 3 tens =
6 tens

Add. Circle the answer if you regrouped.

1.

tens	ones
3	6
+ 1	9

tens	ones
1	7
+ 4	5

tens	ones
2	9
+ 5	4

tens	ones
7	7
+ 1	1

tens	ones
2	2
+ 4	8

2.

tens	ones
7	2
+ 1	8

tens	ones
5	2
+ 4	3

tens	ones
3	5
+ 4	8

tens	ones
6	6
+ 2	4

tens	ones
7	5
+ 1	4

Name_____ Date_____

Add.

1.
$$\begin{array}{r} 38 \\ + 15 \\ \hline 53 \end{array}$$
$$\begin{array}{r} 27 \\ + 17 \\ \hline \end{array}$$
$$\begin{array}{r} 29 \\ + 34 \\ \hline \end{array}$$
$$\begin{array}{r} 68 \\ + 13 \\ \hline \end{array}$$
$$\begin{array}{r} 17 \\ + 45 \\ \hline \end{array}$$

2.
$$\begin{array}{r} 73 \\ + 15 \\ \hline \end{array}$$
$$\begin{array}{r} 39 \\ + 26 \\ \hline \end{array}$$
$$\begin{array}{r} 44 \\ + 16 \\ \hline \end{array}$$
$$\begin{array}{r} 35 \\ + 36 \\ \hline \end{array}$$
$$\begin{array}{r} 16 \\ + 73 \\ \hline \end{array}$$

3.
$$\begin{array}{r} 12 \\ + 72 \\ \hline \end{array}$$
$$\begin{array}{r} 20 \\ + 55 \\ \hline \end{array}$$
$$\begin{array}{r} 19 \\ + 19 \\ \hline \end{array}$$
$$\begin{array}{r} 68 \\ + 15 \\ \hline \end{array}$$
$$\begin{array}{r} 27 \\ + 29 \\ \hline \end{array}$$

4.
$$\begin{array}{r} 25 \\ + 37 \\ \hline \end{array}$$
$$\begin{array}{r} 26 \\ + 22 \\ \hline \end{array}$$
$$\begin{array}{r} 64 \\ + 16 \\ \hline \end{array}$$
$$\begin{array}{r} 13 \\ + 27 \\ \hline \end{array}$$
$$\begin{array}{r} 19 \\ + 39 \\ \hline \end{array}$$

5.
$$\begin{array}{r} 29 \\ + 49 \\ \hline \end{array}$$
$$\begin{array}{r} 25 \\ + 44 \\ \hline \end{array}$$
$$\begin{array}{r} 39 \\ + 18 \\ \hline \end{array}$$
$$\begin{array}{r} 19 \\ + 31 \\ \hline \end{array}$$
$$\begin{array}{r} 32 \\ + 53 \\ \hline \end{array}$$

Name_____ Date_____

tens	ones
3	15
4	5
− 2	8

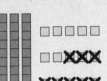

tens	ones
3	15
4	5
− 2	8
	7

tens	ones
3	15
4	5
− 2	8
1	7

You cannot subtract 8 ones from 5 ones. Regroup 1 ten for 10 ones.

Subtract the ones. 15 ones − 8 ones = 7 ones

Subtract the tens. 3 tens − 2 tens = 1 tens 45 − 28 = 17

Subtract. Circle the answer if you regrouped.

1.

tens	ones
3	6
− 1	9

tens	ones
6	8
− 4	5

tens	ones
7	2
− 5	4

tens	ones
5	7
− 1	8

tens	ones
4	8
− 2	2

2.

tens	ones
3	2
− 1	8

tens	ones
5	2
− 4	7

tens	ones
9	8
− 4	8

tens	ones
6	0
− 2	4

tens	ones
7	5
− 1	6

Name_____ Date_____

Subtract. Circle the correct answer.

1.
$$52 - 17$$
35

59   **35**

2.
$$47 - 19$$

28   **38**

3.
$$41 - 22$$

19   **29**

4.
$$63 - 17$$

56   **46**

5.
$$91 - 56$$

35   **45**

6.
$$65 - 16$$

49   **59**

7.
$$42 - 13$$

26   **29**

8.
$$35 - 17$$

18   **19**

9.
$$73 - 67$$

16   **6**

10.
$$34 - 14$$

10   **20**

11.
$$83 - 66$$

17   **27**

12.
$$56 - 28$$

28   **38**

13.
$$90 - 41$$

49   **51**

14.
$$81 - 35$$

46   **56**

15.
$$37 - 29$$

8   **18**

16.
$$70 - 34$$

34   **36**

Regrouping Practice

Name_____ Date_____

Fill in the circle next to the correct answer.

1. 17 + 13 ○ a) 20 ○ b) 30 ○ c) 40	**2.** 52 − 39 ○ a) 11 ○ b) 12 ○ c) 13	**3.** 25 + 16 ○ a) 41 ○ b) 42 ○ c) 43
4. 18 + 14 ○ a) 24 ○ b) 30 ○ c) 32	**5.** 67 − 48 ○ a) 18 ○ b) 19 ○ c) 23	**6.** 54 − 37 ○ a) 15 ○ b) 17 ○ c) 27
7. 25 + 38 ○ a) 53 ○ b) 63 ○ c) 65	**8.** 72 − 56 ○ a) 16 ○ b) 17 ○ c) 26	**9.** 27 + 19 ○ a) 42 ○ b) 44 ○ c) 46
10. 94 − 78 ○ a) 16 ○ b) 26 ○ c) 32	**11.** 16 + 26 ○ a) 24 ○ b) 34 ○ c) 42	**12.** 90 − 73 ○ a) 17 ○ b) 23 ○ c) 27
13. 18 + 23 ○ a) 21 ○ b) 31 ○ c) 41	**14.** 84 − 58 ○ a) 24 ○ b) 26 ○ c) 35	**15.** 39 + 31 ○ a) 60 ○ b) 70 ○ c) 80

Name_____ Date_____

Read each problem. Write a number sentence and solve.

1. Rachel sold 15 candy bars on Monday. On Tuesday she sold 18 more. How many candy bars did Rachel sell in all?

$$\begin{array}{r} 15 \\ + 18 \\ \hline 33 \end{array}$$

2. Jim has 46 baseball cards and 29 football cards. How many sports cards does Jim have in all?

_____

3. David and Al were playing checkers. David won 14 games and Al won 7 games. How many games did they play?

_____

4. There were 23 birds in the tree. 17 more birds joined them. How many birds were in the tree altogether?

_____

5. At the zoo, there are 28 black bears and 28 polar bears. How many bears are there in all?

_____

6. There are 33 red balloons and 29 blue balloons. How many balloons are there altogether?

_____

Word Problems: Addition (III)

Name_____ Date_____

Read each problem. Write a number sentence and solve.

1. The amusement park has 14 roller coasters and 16 kiddie rides. How many rides are there in all?

_____

2. There are 42 boys and 29 girls in line for pizza. How many total children are in line?

_____

3. 75 tickets were collected before noon. 19 more were collected by the end of the day. How many tickets were collected in all?

_____

4. Tina rode the ferris wheel 27 times and the bumper cars 18 times. How many rides did Tina ride in all?

_____

5. Mom watched 13 shows and Dad watched 9 shows. How many shows did they watch altogether?

_____

6. 29 big fireworks and 39 little fireworks lit up the night sky. How many fireworks were there in all?

_____

Word Problems: Subtraction (II)

Name_____ Date_____

Read each problem. Write a number sentence and solve.

1. On Sunday, 35 children were playing in the park. Then 16 of them went home. How many children were still playing?

$$\begin{array}{r} {}^{2}\cancel{3}{}^{15} \\ -16 \\ \hline 19 \end{array}$$

2. There were 41 boys and 28 girls at the park. How many more boys than girls were there?

_____

3. Fred had 74 pieces of paper. He used 49 of them in a book he was writing. How many pieces of paper does Fred have left?

_____

4. 67 people planned to pick up their tickets at the box office. Only 29 of them made it to the game. How many tickets were left?

_____

5. 83 students tried out for the school play. Only 37 of them got parts. How many students did not get a part?

_____

6. Kristen had 52 pairs of shoes. She gave 18 of them to her sister. How many pairs of shoes does Kristen have left?

_____

Name_____ Date_____

Read each problem. Write a number sentence and solve.

1. Mrs. Smith has 33 poodles and 18 boxers. How many more poodles does Mrs. Smith have?

_____

2. The kennel holds 91 dogs. Mr. Glass has 67 dogs in the kennel now. How many spaces does he have left?

_____

3. Mr. Kelly has 44 beagles. 26 of them are puppies. How many adult beagles does Mr. Kelly have?

_____

4. Mrs. Green has 60 terriers. 25 of them are boys. How many terriers are girls?

_____

5. There were 58 kittens at the pet shop on Friday. 29 of them were sold on Saturday. How many kittens were left?

_____

6. Pat counted 22 lizards in the tank at the pet shop. 8 were sold later that day. How many lizards were left in the tank?

_____

Name_____ Date_____

Read each problem. Write a number sentence and solve.

1. Mark sells 27 vanilla shakes and 35 chocolate shakes. How many shakes does Mark sell in all?

_____

2. Sue sold 53 hot dogs and 36 hamburgers. How many more hot dogs did Sue sell?

_____

3. Todd prepared 85 bags of cotton candy. He sold 57 of them. How many bags of cotton candy were left?

_____

4. Patty sold 61 pretzels with salt and 19 pretzels without salt. How many pretzels did Patty sell altogether?

_____

5. Justin sells 42 bags of popcorn with butter and 29 without butter. How many bags of popcorn does Justin sell in all?

_____

6. Amy has 38 ride tickets. She needs 72 tickets to ride all the rides. How many more tickets does Amy need?

_____

Hundreds, Tens, and Ones (1)

Name_____ Date_____

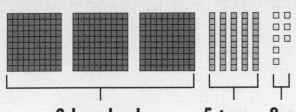 

3 hundreds   5 tens   8 ones

Write how many hundreds, tens, and ones. Then write the number.

1.

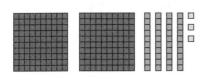

_____ hundreds _____ tens

_____ ones   = _____

2.

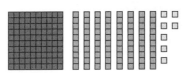

_____ hundreds _____ tens

_____ ones   = _____

3.

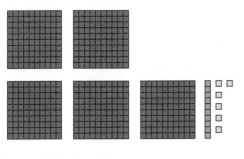

_____ hundreds _____ tens

_____ ones   = _____

4.

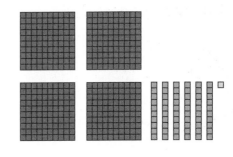

_____ hundreds _____ tens

_____ ones   = _____

5.

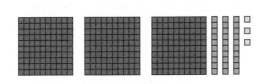

_____ hundreds _____ tens

_____ ones   = _____

6.

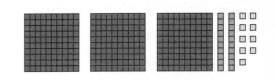

_____ hundreds _____ tens

_____ ones   = _____

Name_____ Date_____

Read the riddles. Write the number.

1. I have 3 hundreds, 6 tens, and 5 ones. What number am I?

   _____365_____

2. I have 8 hundreds, 2 ones, and 5 tens. What number am I?

   _____

3. I have 4 tens, 7 hundreds, and 6 ones. What number am I?

   _____

4. I have 3 ones, 9 hundreds, and 2 tens. What number am I?

   _____

5. I have the same number of hundreds, tens, and ones. I have 4 tens. What number am I?

   _____

6. I have the same number of hundreds, tens, and ones. I have 1 one. What number am I?

   _____

7. I have 4 ones and 1 ten. I am between 610 and 620. What number am I?

   _____

8. I have 3 tens and 9 ones. I am between 500 and 600. What number am I?

   _____

9. I have 8 ones and 2 hundreds. I am between 270 and 280. What number am I?

   _____

10. I have 5 hundreds and 3 ones. I am more than 590. What number am I?

    _____

Numbers: Expanded Form

Name_____ Date_____

Write the numeral.

1. 300 + 40 + 2 = __342__   900 + 30 + 1 = _____

2. 500 + 60 + 7 = _____   400 + 70 + 4 = _____

3. 200 + 10 + 9 = _____   600 + 40 + 3 = _____

4. 100 + 90 + 6 = _____   800 + 20 + 6 = _____

5. 700 + 80 + 5 = _____   100 + 20 + 3 = _____

Write the expanded form of each numeral.

6. 149 = __100__ + __40__ + __9__   267 = ____ + ____ + ___

7. 532 = ____ + ____ + ___   451 = ____ + ____ + ___

8. 728 = ____ + ____ + ___   986 = ____ + ____ + ___

9. 314 = ____ + ____ + ___   698 = ____ + ____ + ___

10. 873 = ____ + ____ + ___   555 = ____ + ____ + ___

Numbers: Word Form

Name_____ Date_____

Match.

One hundred thirty-five	678
Six hundred seventy-eight	135
Four hundred twenty-three	517
Five hundred seventeen	809
Seven hundred thirty-four	423
Eight hundred nine	342
Three hundred forty-two	290
Nine hundred sixty-one	734
Two hundred ninety	209
One hundred seventy-five	900
Six hundred fifty-seven	961
Nine hundred	432
Four hundred thirty-two	657
Two hundred nine	175

Name_____ Date_____

Write the number for each clue.

Across
A. 4 hundreds 2 tens 6 ones
B. Eight hundred five
D. 200 + 70 + 8
F. Five hundred thirty-seven
G. 7 hundreds 2 tens 9 ones
I. Four hundred seventy-six
K. 800 + 10 + 2
L. Four hundred

Down
A. 400 + 90 + 2
C. 5 hundreds 1 ten 7 ones
E. Eight hundred sixty-nine
F. 500 + 70 + 4
H. 2 hundreds 3 tens 1 one
J. Seven hundred ninety

Name_____ Date_____

hundreds	tens	ones
1	4	7
+ 5	3	2
		9

Add the ones.
7 ones + 2 ones = 9 ones

hundreds	tens	ones
1	4	7
+ 5	3	2
	7	

Add the tens.
4 tens + 3 tens = 7 tens

hundreds	tens	ones
1	4	7
+ 5	3	2
6		

Add the hundreds.
1 hundred + 5 hundreds =
6 hundreds
The sum is 679.

First add the ones. Then add the tens. Then add the hundreds.

1.

hundreds	tens	ones
5	1	6
+ 2	8	0

hundreds	tens	ones
3	4	0
+ 5	1	8

hundreds	tens	ones
9	4	1
+	2	8

2.

hundreds	tens	ones
3	2	6
+ 4	5	3

hundreds	tens	ones
4	3	6
+ 5	3	0

hundreds	tens	ones
8	2	1
+ 1	6	2

3.

hundreds	tens	ones
	3	4
+ 8	5	4

hundreds	tens	ones
1	5	2
+ 7	4	2

hundreds	tens	ones
6	0	7
+ 2	5	1

4.

hundreds	tens	ones
2	1	4
+ 3	2	3

hundreds	tens	ones
4	0	1
+ 2	1	4

hundreds	tens	ones
1	5	1
+ 2	4	1

Three-Digit Addition (II)

Name_____ Date_____

Add. Circle the correct answer.

1.
```
  524
+ 173
  697
```
(697) **491**

2.
```
  452
+ 141
```
591 **593**

3.
```
  641
+ 223
```
964 **864**

4.
```
  730
+ 145
```
875 **675**

5.
```
  162
+ 312
```
450 **474**

6.
```
  814
+ 102
```
916 **961**

7.
```
  103
+ 224
```
327 **127**

8.
```
  638
+ 111
```
649 **749**

9.
```
  121
+ 101
```
222 **244**

10.
```
  450
+ 210
```
651 **660**

11.
```
  216
+ 222
```
434 **438**

12.
```
  332
+ 655
```
987 **876**

13.
```
  500
+ 210
```
701 **710**

14.
```
  421
+ 141
```
562 **583**

15.
```
  114
+ 120
```
244 **234**

16.
```
  254
+ 145
```
199 **399**

Three-Digit Addition (III)

Name_____ Date_____

Add. Circle the sums that are greater than 599.

What pattern do you see?_____

1.
$$200 + 400 = 600$$ $$279 + 110$$ $$412 + 213$$ $$342 + 247$$ $$168 + 321$$

2.
$$240 + 410$$ $$353 + 322$$ $$152 + 345$$ $$412 + 87$$ $$253 + 243$$

3.
$$509 + 50$$ $$400 + 300$$ $$620 + 105$$ $$321 + 123$$ $$230 + 520$$

4.
$$327 + 261$$ $$316 + 282$$ $$443 + 332$$ $$400 + 400$$ $$258 + 341$$

5.
$$622 + 203$$ $$313 + 130$$ $$500 + 350$$ $$674 + 201$$ $$600 + 300$$

Adding Three Numbers

Name_____ Date_____

Add.

1.
$$\begin{array}{r} 407 \\ 201 \\ +\,301 \\ \hline \end{array}$$
$$\begin{array}{r} 105 \\ 263 \\ +\,310 \\ \hline \end{array}$$
$$\begin{array}{r} 613 \\ 273 \\ +\,102 \\ \hline \end{array}$$
$$\begin{array}{r} 562 \\ 202 \\ +\,101 \\ \hline \end{array}$$
$$\begin{array}{r} 130 \\ 124 \\ +\,112 \\ \hline \end{array}$$

2.
$$\begin{array}{r} 201 \\ 332 \\ +\,243 \\ \hline \end{array}$$
$$\begin{array}{r} 230 \\ 618 \\ +\,151 \\ \hline \end{array}$$
$$\begin{array}{r} 301 \\ 121 \\ +\,131 \\ \hline \end{array}$$
$$\begin{array}{r} 243 \\ 433 \\ +\,200 \\ \hline \end{array}$$
$$\begin{array}{r} 101 \\ 220 \\ +\,111 \\ \hline \end{array}$$

3.
$$\begin{array}{r} 160 \\ 210 \\ +\,500 \\ \hline \end{array}$$
$$\begin{array}{r} 212 \\ 321 \\ +\,231 \\ \hline \end{array}$$
$$\begin{array}{r} 140 \\ 131 \\ +\,220 \\ \hline \end{array}$$
$$\begin{array}{r} 264 \\ 211 \\ +\,114 \\ \hline \end{array}$$
$$\begin{array}{r} 302 \\ 302 \\ +\,302 \\ \hline \end{array}$$

4.
$$\begin{array}{r} 183 \\ 101 \\ +\,110 \\ \hline \end{array}$$
$$\begin{array}{r} 201 \\ 342 \\ +\,142 \\ \hline \end{array}$$
$$\begin{array}{r} 201 \\ 162 \\ +\,230 \\ \hline \end{array}$$
$$\begin{array}{r} 413 \\ 271 \\ +\,203 \\ \hline \end{array}$$
$$\begin{array}{r} 523 \\ 120 \\ +\,102 \\ \hline \end{array}$$

Three-Digit Addition: Regrouping (1)

Name_____ Date_____

hundreds	tens	ones
	1	
2	5	8
+ 3	9	4
		2

Add the ones. There are 12 ones. Regroup 10 ones for 1 ten.

hundreds	tens	ones
1	1	
2	5	8
+ 3	9	4
	5	2

Add the tens. There are 15 tens. Regroup 10 tens for 1 hundred.

hundreds	tens	ones
1	1	
2	5	8
+ 3	9	4
6	5	2

Add the hundreds. There are 6 hundreds. The sum is 652.

Add. Circle the answer if you regrouped.

1.

hundreds	tens	ones
4	3	2
+ 2	8	3

hundreds	tens	ones
2	4	8
+ 3	4	6

hundreds	tens	ones
2	5	6
+ 3	3	3

2.

hundreds	tens	ones
3	6	5
+ 3	7	9

hundreds	tens	ones
1	2	5
+ 3	3	1

hundreds	tens	ones
5	1	4
+ 3	2	8

3.

hundreds	tens	ones
7	8	4
+ 1	6	5

hundreds	tens	ones
2	9	4
+ 3	2	3

hundreds	tens	ones
2	3	4
+ 1	6	4

Name_____ Date_____

Add.

1.
$$\begin{array}{r} 328 \\ + 155 \\ \hline 483 \end{array}$$
$$\begin{array}{r} 237 \\ + 139 \\ \hline \end{array}$$
$$\begin{array}{r} 284 \\ + 334 \\ \hline \end{array}$$
$$\begin{array}{r} 683 \\ + 133 \\ \hline \end{array}$$
$$\begin{array}{r} 170 \\ + 452 \\ \hline \end{array}$$

2.
$$\begin{array}{r} 734 \\ + 154 \\ \hline \end{array}$$
$$\begin{array}{r} 391 \\ + 262 \\ \hline \end{array}$$
$$\begin{array}{r} 424 \\ + 126 \\ \hline \end{array}$$
$$\begin{array}{r} 357 \\ + 362 \\ \hline \end{array}$$
$$\begin{array}{r} 152 \\ + 738 \\ \hline \end{array}$$

3.
$$\begin{array}{r} 174 \\ + 773 \\ \hline \end{array}$$
$$\begin{array}{r} 209 \\ + 551 \\ \hline \end{array}$$
$$\begin{array}{r} 194 \\ + 193 \\ \hline \end{array}$$
$$\begin{array}{r} 682 \\ + 152 \\ \hline \end{array}$$
$$\begin{array}{r} 273 \\ + 296 \\ \hline \end{array}$$

4.
$$\begin{array}{r} 253 \\ + 371 \\ \hline \end{array}$$
$$\begin{array}{r} 206 \\ + 202 \\ \hline \end{array}$$
$$\begin{array}{r} 641 \\ + 167 \\ \hline \end{array}$$
$$\begin{array}{r} 133 \\ + 276 \\ \hline \end{array}$$
$$\begin{array}{r} 197 \\ + 390 \\ \hline \end{array}$$

5.
$$\begin{array}{r} 298 \\ + 491 \\ \hline \end{array}$$
$$\begin{array}{r} 253 \\ + 442 \\ \hline \end{array}$$
$$\begin{array}{r} 394 \\ + 182 \\ \hline \end{array}$$
$$\begin{array}{r} 176 \\ + 117 \\ \hline \end{array}$$
$$\begin{array}{r} 321 \\ + 530 \\ \hline \end{array}$$

Name_____ Date_____

Write the sum for each clue.

Across

A. 227
  + 96

F. 47
  + 110

J. 518
  + 342

C. 470
  + 219

H. 169
  + 379

K. 494
  + 459

E. 86
  + 148

Down

A. 198
  + 163

C. 318
  + 327

I. 336
  + 89

B. 225
  + 102

D. 381
  + 547

J. 59
  + 28

G. 257
  + 249

Three-Digit Subtraction (1)

hundreds	tens	ones
8	4	9
− 5	1	2
		7

Subtract the ones.
9 ones − 2 ones = 7 ones

hundreds	tens	ones
8	4	9
− 5	1	2
	3	7

Subtract the tens.
4 tens − 1 ten = 3 tens

hundreds	tens	ones
8	4	9
− 5	1	2
3	3	7

Subtract the hundreds.
8 hundreds − 5 hundreds = 3 hundreds
The sum is 337.

Unit 2

Subtract.

1.

hundreds	tens	ones
9	7	6
− 3	5	3

hundreds	tens	ones
7	8	5
− 4	8	1

hundreds	tens	ones
8	9	9
− 4	4	1

2.

hundreds	tens	ones
5	8	6
− 2	5	4

hundreds	tens	ones
8	3	6
− 5	2	0

hundreds	tens	ones
9	7	5
− 2	3	4

3.

hundreds	tens	ones
4	9	8
− 2	5	1

hundreds	tens	ones
3	9	2
−	9	2

hundreds	tens	ones
6	4	7
− 3	2	5

Three-Digit Subtraction (II)

Name_____ Date_____

Subtract. Circle the correct answer.

1.
$$\begin{array}{r} 524 \\ -\ 123 \\ \hline \end{array}$$

421   **401**

2.
$$\begin{array}{r} 452 \\ -\ 141 \\ \hline \end{array}$$

511   **311**

3.
$$\begin{array}{r} 748 \\ -\ 223 \\ \hline \end{array}$$

525   **625**

4.
$$\begin{array}{r} 787 \\ -\ 145 \\ \hline \end{array}$$

642   **643**

5.
$$\begin{array}{r} 662 \\ -\ 312 \\ \hline \end{array}$$

350   **250**

6.
$$\begin{array}{r} 814 \\ -\ 102 \\ \hline \end{array}$$

716   **712**

7.
$$\begin{array}{r} 969 \\ -\ 224 \\ \hline \end{array}$$

745   **645**

8.
$$\begin{array}{r} 798 \\ -\ 512 \\ \hline \end{array}$$

649   **286**

9.
$$\begin{array}{r} 939 \\ -\ 100 \\ \hline \end{array}$$

839   **739**

10.
$$\begin{array}{r} 454 \\ -\ 331 \\ \hline \end{array}$$

123   **132**

11.
$$\begin{array}{r} 657 \\ -\ 213 \\ \hline \end{array}$$

434   **444**

12.
$$\begin{array}{r} 839 \\ -\ 232 \\ \hline \end{array}$$

567   **607**

13.
$$\begin{array}{r} 464 \\ -\ 210 \\ \hline \end{array}$$

654   **254**

14.
$$\begin{array}{r} 884 \\ -\ 321 \\ \hline \end{array}$$

653   **563**

15.
$$\begin{array}{r} 954 \\ -\ 152 \\ \hline \end{array}$$

802   **806**

16.
$$\begin{array}{r} 297 \\ -\ 121 \\ \hline \end{array}$$

176   **186**

Name_____ Date_____

Subtract.

1.
$$\begin{array}{r} 378 \\ -155 \\ \hline \end{array}$$
$$\begin{array}{r} 239 \\ -139 \\ \hline \end{array}$$
$$\begin{array}{r} 688 \\ -334 \\ \hline \end{array}$$
$$\begin{array}{r} 683 \\ -133 \\ \hline \end{array}$$
$$\begin{array}{r} 979 \\ -512 \\ \hline \end{array}$$

2.
$$\begin{array}{r} 796 \\ -154 \\ \hline \end{array}$$
$$\begin{array}{r} 398 \\ -262 \\ \hline \end{array}$$
$$\begin{array}{r} 427 \\ -126 \\ \hline \end{array}$$
$$\begin{array}{r} 397 \\ -167 \\ \hline \end{array}$$
$$\begin{array}{r} 858 \\ -738 \\ \hline \end{array}$$

3.
$$\begin{array}{r} 774 \\ -472 \\ \hline \end{array}$$
$$\begin{array}{r} 589 \\ -101 \\ \hline \end{array}$$
$$\begin{array}{r} 794 \\ -183 \\ \hline \end{array}$$
$$\begin{array}{r} 687 \\ -145 \\ \hline \end{array}$$
$$\begin{array}{r} 576 \\ -263 \\ \hline \end{array}$$

4.
$$\begin{array}{r} 983 \\ -321 \\ \hline \end{array}$$
$$\begin{array}{r} 356 \\ -216 \\ \hline \end{array}$$
$$\begin{array}{r} 698 \\ -423 \\ \hline \end{array}$$
$$\begin{array}{r} 988 \\ -576 \\ \hline \end{array}$$
$$\begin{array}{r} 897 \\ -390 \\ \hline \end{array}$$

5.
$$\begin{array}{r} 799 \\ -411 \\ \hline \end{array}$$
$$\begin{array}{r} 873 \\ -142 \\ \hline \end{array}$$
$$\begin{array}{r} 398 \\ -182 \\ \hline \end{array}$$
$$\begin{array}{r} 577 \\ -117 \\ \hline \end{array}$$
$$\begin{array}{r} 989 \\ -530 \\ \hline \end{array}$$

Subtracting More Than Once

Name_____ Date_____

Subtract.

1. 549	2. 677	3. 289	4. 488	5. 976
− 134	− 225	− 131	− 123	− 412
415				
− 204	− 251	− 126	− 105	− 312
211				
− 101	− 101	− 40	− 230	− 41
110				

6. 888	7. 796	8. 999	9. 574	10. 697
− 241	− 313	− 452	− 120	− 13
− 213	− 140	− 100	− 150	− 31
− 122	− 211	− 321	− 102	− 310
− 211	− 112	− 101	− 100	− 130

Name_____ Date_____

hundreds	tens	ones
7	3	9
− 4	5	3
		6

Subtract the ones.
9 ones − 3 ones = 6 ones

hundreds	tens	ones
	6 13	
7	3	9
− 4	5	3
	8	6

You cannot subtract 5 tens
from 3 tens. Regroup
1 hundred for 10 tens.
Subtract the tens.
13 tens − 5 tens = 8 tens

hundreds	tens	ones
	6 13	
7	3	9
− 4	5	3
2	8	6

Subtract the hundreds.
6 hundreds − 4 hundreds =
2 hundreds
The difference is 286.

Unit 2

Subtract. Circle the answer if you regrouped.

1.

hundreds	tens	ones
5	3	9
− 1	8	7

hundreds	tens	ones
7	5	2
− 3	4	6

hundreds	tens	ones
6	4	6
− 5	3	3

2.

hundreds	tens	ones
8	6	5
− 3	7	1

hundreds	tens	ones
7	9	7
− 6	4	7

hundreds	tens	ones
6	8	4
− 1	6	5

3.

hundreds	tens	ones
9	5	6
− 3	3	1

hundreds	tens	ones
8	7	3
− 6	3	5

hundreds	tens	ones
8	7	1
− 1	2	9

Name_____ Date_____

Subtract.

1.
$$230 - 116 = 114$$
  $$456 - 126$$
  $$946 - 753$$
  $$632 - 392$$
  $$833 - 418$$

2.
$$495 - 178$$
  $$434 - 254$$
  $$829 - 340$$
  $$667 - 318$$
  $$762 - 111$$

3.
$$950 - 428$$
  $$963 - 182$$
  $$754 - 251$$
  $$772 - 549$$
  $$461 - 371$$

4.
$$489 - 144$$
  $$538 - 161$$
  $$790 - 145$$
  $$656 - 409$$
  $$727 - 208$$

5.
$$950 - 112$$
  $$733 - 281$$
  $$362 - 126$$
  $$337 - 124$$
  $$929 - 430$$

Name_____ Date_____

Subtract. Then color the box on the bingo card that shows the answer. When you have colored five in a row, you have won Bingo!

1.
```
   527        838        645        603
 - 376      - 512      - 391      - 133
```

2.
```
   854        429        836        600
 - 206      - 122      - 243      - 400
```

3.
```
   398        594        705        877
 - 123      - 387      - 623      - 258
```

4.
```
   502        579        567        704
 - 352      - 121      - 471      - 203
```

B	I	N	G	O
151	307	254	684	458
275	470	111	207	326
75	82	501	620	900
619	520	69	648	200
150	371	593	507	96

Regrouping Practice (1)

Name_____ Date_____

Fill in the circle next to the correct answer.

1. $\begin{array}{r} 172 \\ + 133 \\ \hline \end{array}$ ○ a) 205 ○ b) 305 ○ c) 315	2. $\begin{array}{r} 612 \\ - 390 \\ \hline \end{array}$ ○ a) 222 ○ b) 302 ○ c) 322	3. $\begin{array}{r} 254 \\ + 244 \\ \hline \end{array}$ ○ a) 410 ○ b) 489 ○ c) 498
4. $\begin{array}{r} 509 \\ + 106 \\ \hline \end{array}$ ○ a) 403 ○ b) 605 ○ c) 615	5. $\begin{array}{r} 990 \\ - 280 \\ \hline \end{array}$ ○ a) 610 ○ b) 701 ○ c) 710	6. $\begin{array}{r} 470 \\ - 370 \\ \hline \end{array}$ ○ a) 100 ○ b) 700 ○ c) 840
7. $\begin{array}{r} 241 \\ + 286 \\ \hline \end{array}$ ○ a) 517 ○ b) 527 ○ c) 572	8. $\begin{array}{r} 990 \\ - 146 \\ \hline \end{array}$ ○ a) 844 ○ b) 856 ○ c) 867	9. $\begin{array}{r} 137 \\ + 136 \\ \hline \end{array}$ ○ a) 237 ○ b) 261 ○ c) 273
10. $\begin{array}{r} 864 \\ - 328 \\ \hline \end{array}$ ○ a) 442 ○ b) 532 ○ c) 536	11. $\begin{array}{r} 221 \\ + 425 \\ \hline \end{array}$ ○ a) 466 ○ b) 646 ○ c) 664	12. $\begin{array}{r} 716 \\ - 153 \\ \hline \end{array}$ ○ a) 563 ○ b) 663 ○ c) 863
13. $\begin{array}{r} 414 \\ + 325 \\ \hline \end{array}$ ○ a) 739 ○ b) 740 ○ c) 838	14. $\begin{array}{r} 877 \\ - 574 \\ \hline \end{array}$ ○ a) 202 ○ b) 241 ○ c) 303	15. $\begin{array}{r} 213 \\ + 272 \\ \hline \end{array}$ ○ a) 458 ○ b) 485 ○ c) 584

Regrouping Practice (II)

Name _____ Date _____

Fill in the circle next to the correct answer.

1.
```
  242
+ 281
```
○ a) 523
○ b) 532
○ c) 541

2.
```
  387
- 216
```
○ a) 101
○ b) 117
○ c) 171

3.
```
  489
+ 340
```
○ a) 729
○ b) 829
○ c) 892

4.
```
  665
+ 273
```
○ a) 438
○ b) 838
○ c) 938

5.
```
  781
- 669
```
○ a) 110
○ b) 112
○ c) 121

6.
```
  647
- 373
```
○ a) 274
○ b) 275
○ c) 324

7.
```
  375
+ 332
```
○ a) 607
○ b) 707
○ c) 770

8.
```
  721
- 414
```
○ a) 307
○ b) 407
○ c) 437

9.
```
  193
+ 195
```
○ a) 284
○ b) 377
○ c) 388

10.
```
  645
- 218
```
○ a) 375
○ b) 427
○ c) 473

11.
```
  454
+ 361
```
○ a) 815
○ b) 851
○ c) 913

12.
```
  798
- 345
```
○ a) 333
○ b) 345
○ c) 453

13.
```
  184
+ 212
```
○ a) 396
○ b) 496
○ c) 596

14.
```
  963
- 217
```
○ a) 556
○ b) 565
○ c) 746

15.
```
  293
+ 361
```
○ a) 456
○ b) 654
○ c) 674

Name_____ Date_____

Read each problem. Write a number sentence and solve.

1. One day, Mr. Carter sells 132 solid white golf balls and 257 striped golf balls. How many golf balls does he sell that day?

$$
\begin{array}{r}
132 \\
+\ 257 \\
\hline
389
\end{array}
$$

2. Mr. Carter orders 268 youth footballs and 527 junior footballs. How many footballs does Mr. Carter order?

_____

3. The booster club buys 375 short sleeve t-shirts and 297 long sleeve t-shirts. How many t-shirts does the club buy?

_____

4. Julie's soccer team buys 328 shiny hair ribbons and 480 satin hair ribbons. How many hair ribbons does the team buy?

_____

5. Mrs. James buys 249 bat stickers and 518 baseball stickers. How many stickers does Mrs. James buy?

_____

6. Tucker buys 125 blue golf tees and 87 yellow golf tees. How many golf tees does Tucker buy?

_____

Name_____ Date_____

Unit 2

Read each problem. Write a number sentence and solve.

1. Mike bought a CD player and a CD. How many tokens did he spend?

$$\begin{array}{r} 509 \\ + 187 \\ \hline 696 \end{array}$$

2. Trevor bought two posters. How many tokens did he spend?

_____

3. Jill bought a jewelry box and a nacklace. How many tokens did she spend?

_____

4. Gina bought a TV and a poster. How many tokens did she spend?

_____

5. John bought two jerseys. How many tokens did he spend?

_____

6. Ashley bought a necklace and a CD. How many tokens did she spend?

_____

7. Who spent the most tokens?

_____

8. Who spent the fewest tokens?

_____

Name_____ Date_____

Read each problem. Write a number sentence and solve.

1. There are 387 boys and 410 girls at the soccer game. How many more girls than boys are at the game?

$$\begin{array}{r} 410 \\ -\ 387 \\ \hline 23 \end{array}$$

_____

2. There are 797 children and 912 adults at the soccer game. How many more adults than children are at the game?

_____

3. The soccer club sells 564 pennants. Of those, 181 are small pennants. How many large pennants are sold?

_____

4. Jane sells 459 bags of peanuts and 953 hot dogs. How many more hot dogs than peanuts are sold?

_____

5. Mr. Nelson has 800 soccer t-shirts to sell. He sells all but 282 of them. How many t-shirts does Mr. Nelson sell?

_____

6. The soccer players give away 175 water bottles. All but 38 of them are given to children. How many water bottles are given to children?

_____

Name_____ Date_____

Read each problem. Write a number sentence and solve.

1. Of a total of 612 children at the movies, 386 are girls. How many boys are at the movies?

_____

2. There are 612 children and 475 adults at the movies. How many more children than adults are at the movies?

_____

3. Mr. Anderson bought 275 sodas. Only 158 children wanted a drink. How many sodas did Mr. Anderson have left?

_____

4. The theater sells 502 bags of popcorn. Of those, 419 are regular-size bags, and the rest are super-size. How many super-size bags of popcorn are sold?

_____

5. Mrs. Young had 385 candy bars. She gave away 150 of them. How many candy bars did Mrs. Young have left?

_____

6. 81 minutes of the movie has been seen. The movie is 123 minutes long. How many more minutes are left?

_____

Name_____ Date_____

Read each problem. Write a number sentence and solve.

1. There was 380 students who went to the zoo. Of those, 237 were boys. How many girls went to the zoo?

_____

2. 110 students liked the stegosaurus and 97 liked the brontosaurus. How many students liked the dinsaurs?

_____

3. George counted 441 fossils on the wall. Then he saw 129 on the ground. How many fossils were there altogether?

_____

4. 465 tours were given on Monday. On Saturday, 748 tours were given. How many more tours were given on Saturday?

_____

5. Joe bought a dinosaur book with 584 pictures. The pages came loose and all but 137 pictures fell out. How many dinosaur pictures were lost?

_____

6. Cathy bought 114 postcards while at the museum. Her teacher bought 247 postcards. How many did they buy altogether?

_____

Counting to 999

Write the missing numbers.

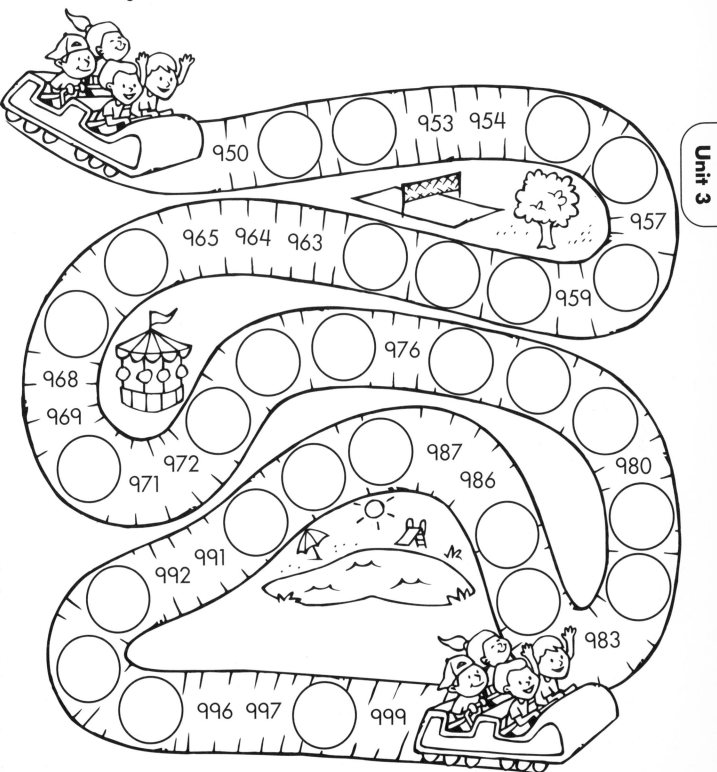

Unit 3

950   953 954

957

965 964 963   959

968   976

969

972   987   980

971   986

992 991   983

996 997   999

Odd and Even Numbers

Name_____ Date_____

Odd numbers end in **1**, **3**, **5**, **7**, and **9**.

Even numbers end in **0**, **2**, **4**, **6**, and **8**.

Circle the **odd** numbers.

1.	142	157	423	916	235	374
2.	287	428	456	195	607	550
3.	121	169	176	724	930	173
4.	494	547	231	189	100	422

Circle the **even** numbers.

5.	765	810	973	522	436	343
6.	198	289	321	676	487	420
7.	222	121	549	853	950	678
8.	555	624	508	233	711	165

Count how many you circled for each. Write the number.

9. _____ odd numbers   10. _____ even numbers

Name_____ Date_____

225   **226**   227   228

226 comes before 227.

Circle the number that comes **before**.

1. I am before 377.
What number am I?

(376)   378   477

2. I am before 899.
What number am I?

909   989   889

3. I am before 171.
What number am I?

161   181   371

4. I am before 234.
What number am I?

254   244   224

5. I am before 506.
What number am I?

606   490   510

6. I am before 615.
What number am I?

675   645   605

7. I am before 982.
What number am I?

999   992   972

8. I am before 803.
What number am I?

813   793   903

Number Order: After

556   557   **558**   559

558 comes after 557.

Write the number that comes **after**.

1. 679 _____   423 _____   918 _____

2. 512 _____   329 _____   789 _____

3. 800 _____   184 _____   222 _____

4. 998 _____   437 _____   525 _____

5. 199 _____   749 _____   101 _____

6. 334 _____   656 _____   799 _____

Number Order: Between

Name_____ Date_____

$$\overline{\quad|\qquad\qquad|\qquad\qquad|\quad}$$

333   **334**   **335**

334 comes between 333 and 335.

335

334

333

Write the number that comes **between**.

1. 269 _____ 271   414 _____ 416

2. 551 _____ 553   668 _____ 670

3. 883 _____ 885   940 _____ 942

4. 312 _____ 314   525 _____ 527

5. 746 _____ 748   399 _____ 401

6. 177 _____ 179   289 _____ 291

Write each group of numbers from **greatest** to **least**.
Escribe cada grupo de numeros de lo más grande a lo más pequeño.

1. 312   123   231   _____ _____ _____

2. 743   634   467   _____ _____ _____

3. 190   214   349   _____ _____ _____

4. 497   528   479   _____ _____ _____

5. 821   757   804   _____ _____ _____

6. 312   321   320   _____ _____ _____

7. 880   816   900   _____ _____ _____

8. 617   600   599   _____ _____ _____

9. 930   929   931   _____ _____ _____

10. 111   101   110   _____ _____ _____

11. 557   576   457   _____ _____ _____

Name_____ Date_____

 **278**  **284**  **297**

Write each group of numbers from **least** to **greatest**. *Escribir cada grupo de numeros de lo mas pequeño a lo más grande.*

1. 475   476   457   <u>457</u>   <u>475</u>   <u>476</u>

2. 590   600   588   _____   _____   _____

3. 355   427   368   _____   _____   _____

4. 878   788   897   _____   _____   _____

5. 112   121   211   _____   _____   _____

6. 999   989   990   _____   _____   _____

7. 463   634   643   _____   _____   _____

8. 777   775   757   _____   _____   _____

9. 246   264   426   _____   _____   _____

10. 600   598   658   _____   _____   _____

11. 333   303   323   _____   _____   _____

Unit 3

Inequality Symbols

Name_____ Date_____

< is less than.
> is greater than.
= is equal to.

Solve. Then compare the answer to the number on the right.
Write **<**, **>**, or **=** to complete each sentence.

1. 475 – 341 ⟨ < ⟩ 150 475 – 341 134	2. 184 + 212 ◯ 325	3. 497 – 265 ◯ 254
4. 131 + 194 ◯ 325	5. 479 – 355 ◯ 100	6. 301 + 402 ◯ 705
7. 146 + 82 ◯ 222	8. 975 – 602 ◯ 334	9. 528 – 427 ◯ 81
10. 745 – 234 ◯ 500	11. 200 + 124 ◯ 324	12. 242 + 359 ◯ 600

Ordinal Numbers

Name_____ Date_____

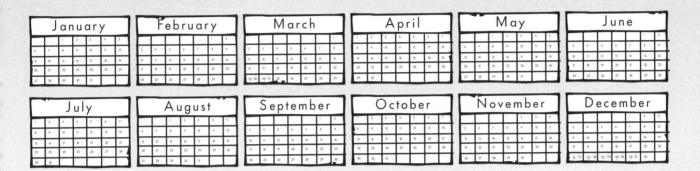

first	second	third	forth	fifth	sixth
seventh	eighth	ninth	tenth	eleventh	twelfth

Write the ordinal number to complete each statement.

1. March is the _____ month of the year.

2. June is the _____ month of the year.

3. November is the_____ month of the year.

4. July is the _____ month of the year.

5. August is the _____ month of the year.

6. February is the _____ month of the year.

7. April is the _____ month of the year.

8. January is the _____ month of the year.

Number Order Practice

Name_____ Date_____

Write the missing numbers.

1. 771 772 _____ _____ 775 _____ _____

2. 581 _____ _____ 584 _____ _____ _____

3. _____ _____ 993 _____ _____ _____ 997

Write the missing numbers.

4. 453 _____   136 _____ 138   699 _____

5. _____ 310   429 _____ 431   _____ 750

Write **<**, **>**, or **=** to compare the numbers.

6. | 279   280 | | 634   634 | | 879   789 |

7. | 521   512 | | 779   781 | | 392   390 |

Solve the riddles. Write the numbers.

8. I am an even number greater than 987 and less than 989. What number am I?

9. I am an odd number greater than 300 and less than 302. What number am I?

_____   _____

Skip Counting: By 10's

Name________________________________ Date____________________

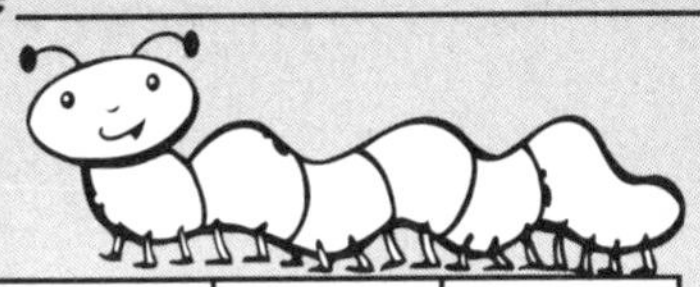

10	20	30	40	50	60	70	80	90	100

Count by 10's. Write the missing numbers.

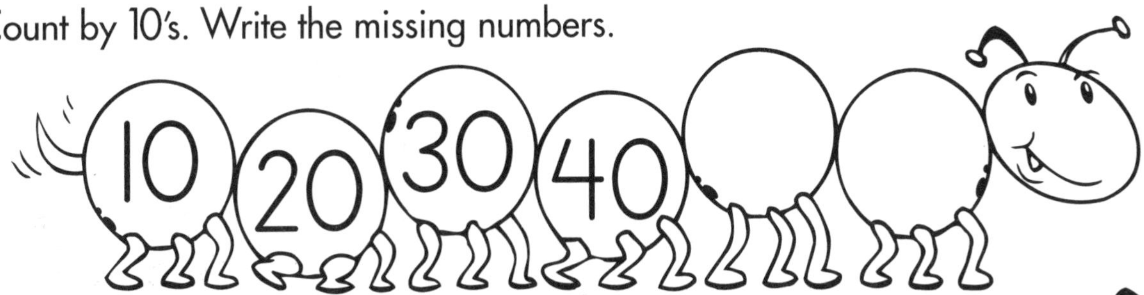
10
20
30
40

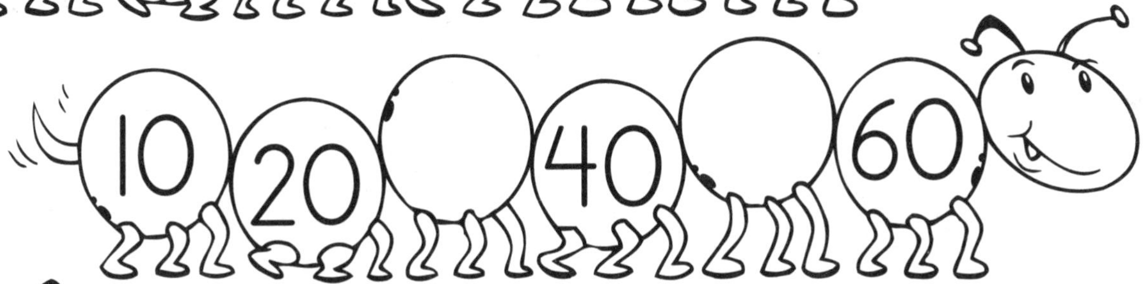
10
20
40
60

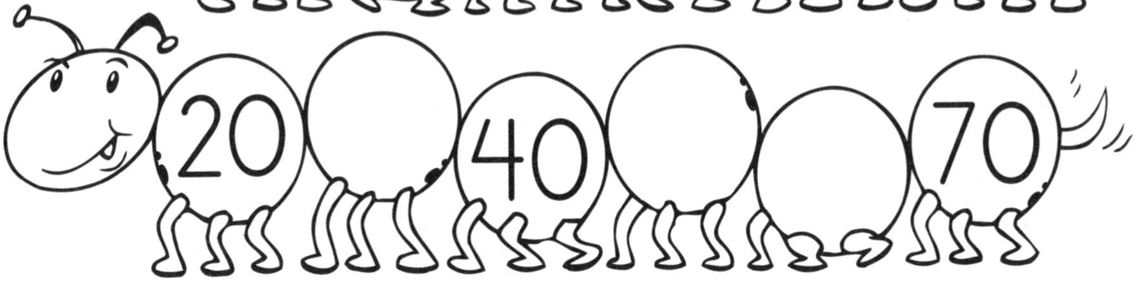
20
40
70

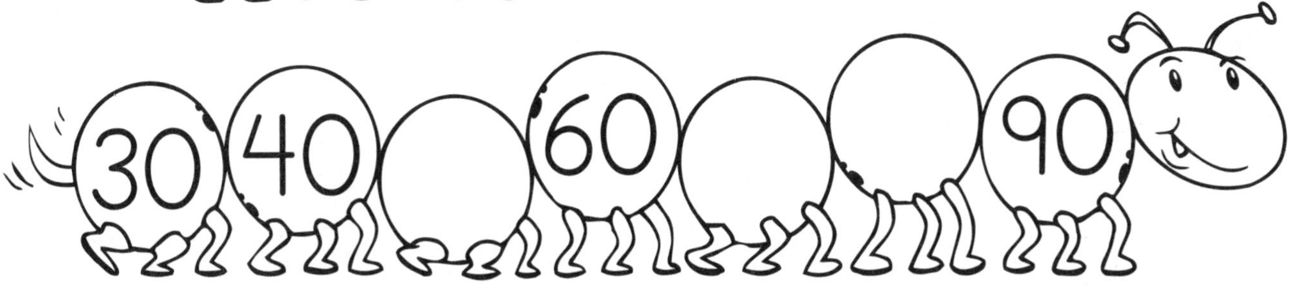
30
40
60
90

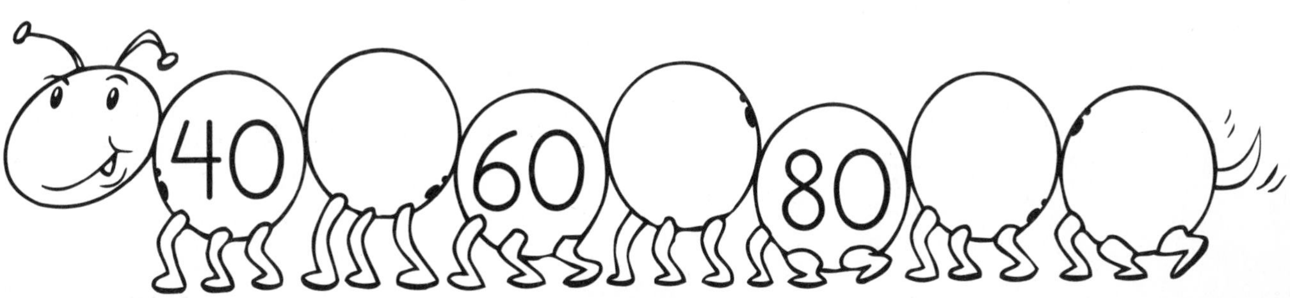
40
60
80

Unit 3

Skip Counting: By 5's

Count by 5's. Draw a path through the maze.

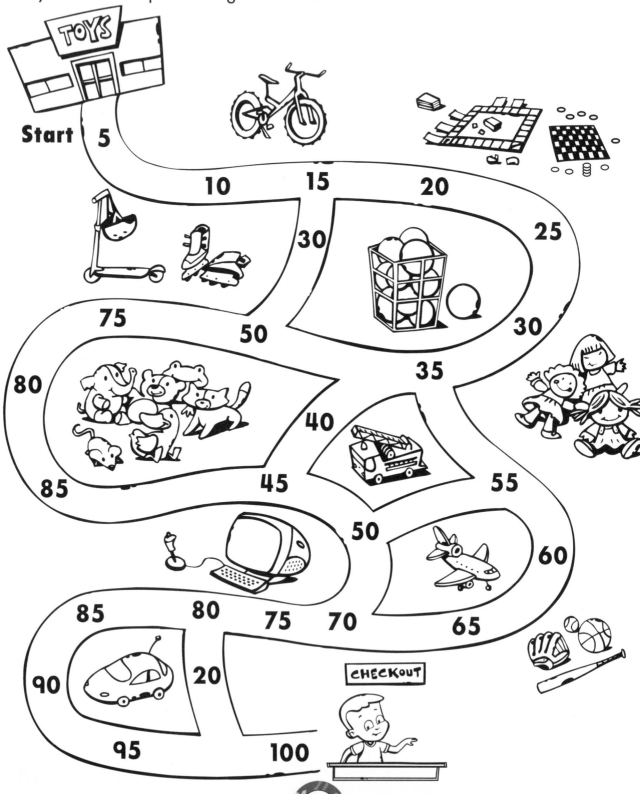

Start   5
10   15   20   25
30   30
75   50   35
80   40   55
85   45   50   60   65
70   75   80   85
20   90
95   100

CHECKOUT

Name_____ Date_____

Count by 2's. Connect the dots.

212
●

216 ●

● 218

Unit 3

214 ●

210 ●

● 220

208
●

● 222

206 ●

224

204 ●

226
●

200 ● ● 230 ● 228

START

202 ●

Name_____ Date_____

Count the ice cream scoops by 3's. Write the number.

1.

_____

2.

_____

3.

_____

4.

_____

5.

_____

Name_____ Date_____

Fill in the missing numbers. Write the rule.

1. 55   60   _____   _____   _____   80   _____

    Rule: _____

2. 6   9   _____   _____   _____   _____   24

    Rule: _____

3. _____   72   _____   76   _____   80   _____

    Rule: _____

4. _____   90   100   _____   120   _____   _____

    Rule: _____

Number Patterns (1)

Name_____ Date_____

Find the pattern. Write the missing numbers.

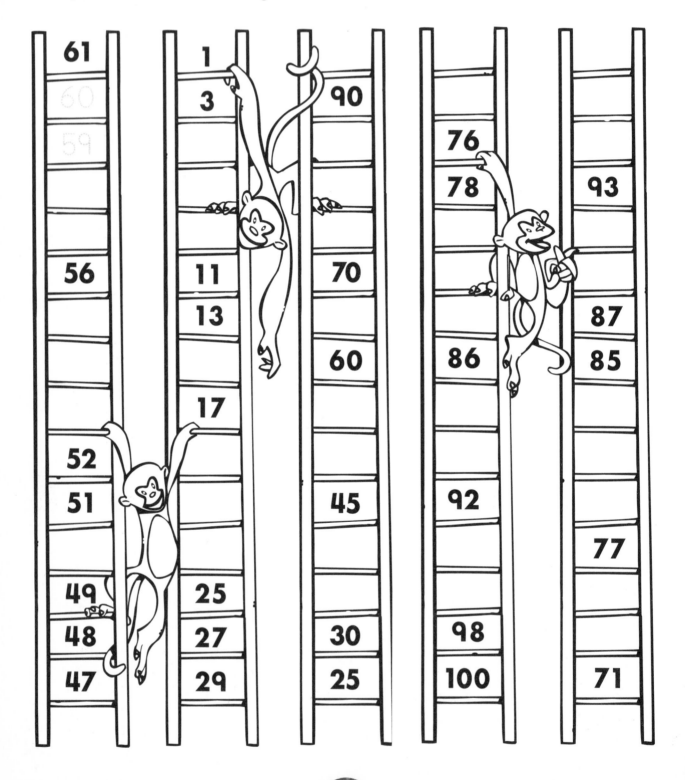

61	1			
60	3	90		
59			76	
			78	93
56	11	70		
	13		86	87
		60	86	85
	17			
52				
51		45	92	
				77
49	25			
48	27	30	98	
47	29	25	100	71

Number Patterns (II)

Name_____ Date_____

Find the patterns. Write the missing numbers.

15	16	17			
	26			30	
		48			

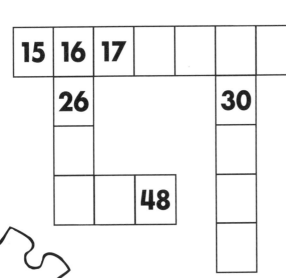

			43
			53
60	61		64
79		83	85
91			

68	67	66	
	57		
36	35	34	
40	42		46

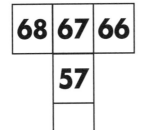

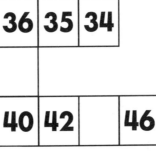

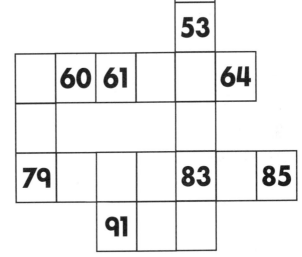

Name_____ Date_____

Draw nickels and pennies to show the amount.

13¢

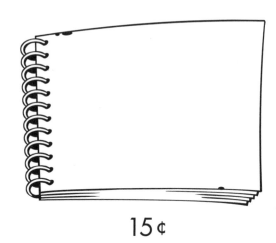

15¢

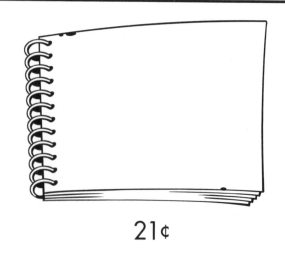

21¢

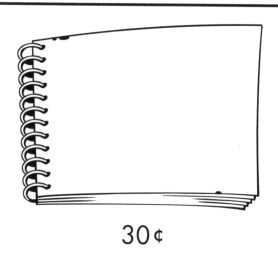

30¢

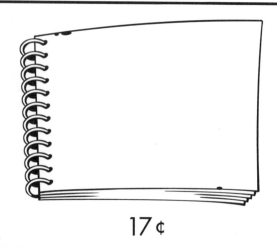

17¢

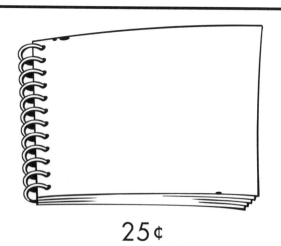

25¢

Name_____ Date_____

Count dimes and pennies. Add to find the total.

1.

_____ ¢   +   _____ ¢   =   _____ ¢

2.

_____ ¢   +   _____ ¢   =   _____ ¢

3.

_____ ¢   +   _____ ¢   =   _____ ¢

4.

_____ ¢   +   _____ ¢   =   _____ ¢

5.

_____ ¢   +   _____ ¢   =   _____ ¢

Name_____ Date_____

Read the riddles. Circle the answers.

Josh has 24¢
in his pocket.
He has 6 coins.
What coins does
Josh have?

Kim has 30¢
in her pocket.
She has 3 coins.
What coins does
Kim have?

Matt has 16¢
in his pocket.
He has 4 coins.
What coins does
Matt have?

Jake has more than 3 nickels,
but less than 2 dimes.

How much money does
Jake have?

Laura has less than 4 nickels,
but more than 8 pennies.

How much money does
Laura have?

18¢   **25¢**   **30¢**   **5¢**   **15¢**   **20¢**

Money: Quarters

Name_____ Date_____

This is a quarter.
A quarter has two sides.

Count the money in each purse. Color the purse if you can trade it for a quarter.

1.

2.

3.

4.

5.

6.

7.

8.

Money Practice (1)

Name_____ Date_____

Start with the coin that is worth the most. Then count on by tens, five, and ones.

25¢   35¢   40¢   45¢   46¢   47¢   **47¢**

Count the coins. Write the amount in the box.

1. _____¢   _____¢   _____¢   _____¢   _____¢   _____¢   _____¢

2. _____¢   _____¢   _____¢   _____¢   _____¢   _____¢   _____¢

3. _____¢   _____¢   _____¢   _____¢   _____¢   _____¢   _____¢

4. _____¢   _____¢   _____¢   _____¢   _____¢   _____¢   _____¢

5. _____¢   _____¢   _____¢   _____¢

Money Practice (II)

Name_____ Date_____

I can use 1 quarter and 1 dime.

35¢

Read the price of each item. Draw the coins you need to buy it. Write the number of coins.

Unit 3

1.
 45¢

25¢   10¢ 10¢

 _____    _____    _____    _____

2.
 64¢

 _____   _____   _____    _____

3.
 30¢

 _____    _____    _____    _____

4.
 42¢

 _____    _____    _____    _____

Money Practice (III)

Name_____ Date_____

Write the letter of the correct answer on the line.

_____ 1.    A. 55¢

_____ 2.   B. $1.30

_____ 3.   C. 9¢

_____ 4.   D. 27¢

_____ 5.   E. 72¢

_____ 6.   F. 14¢

_____ 7.    G. 47¢

_____ 8.   H. 85¢

_____ 9.   I. 35¢

_____ 10.   J. $1.25

Money Word Problems

Name_____ Date_____

Read each problem. Write the answer.

1. You have one dollar, five quarters,
   seven dimes, one nickel and
   five pennies. How much money
   do you have?

   _____ ¢

2. You have three dollars, six quarters,
   one dime, two nickels, and one penny.
   How much money do you have?

   _____ ¢

3. You have two dollars, five quarters,
   seven dimes, four nickels, and
   five pennies. How much money
   do you have?

   _____ ¢

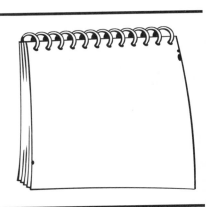

4. You have two dollars, two quarters,
   five dimes, and four pennies. How
   much money do you have?

   _____ ¢

Money Review

Name_____ Date_____

a) **51¢**

b) **61¢**

c) **76¢**

Count the money. Then fill in the circle next to the correct answer.

1.
- a) 54¢
- b) 64¢
- c) 74¢

2.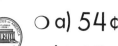
- a) 32¢
- b) 36¢
- c) 52¢

3.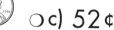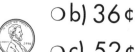
- a) 46¢
- b) 66¢
- c) 88¢

4.
- a) 61¢
- b) 67¢
- c) 71¢

5.
- a) 50¢
- b) 75¢
- c) 85¢

6.
- a) 25¢
- b) 35¢
- c) 75¢

7.
- a) 32¢
- b) 38¢
- c) 42¢

8.
- a) 9¢
- b) 12¢
- c) 15¢

Plane Figures

Name_____ Date_____

A **plane** figure is a shape that is two-dimensional, or flat.

Use the code to color the shapes.

 = blue

 = red

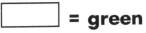 = yellow

 = green

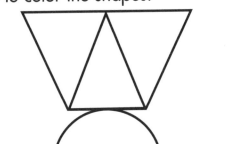

Solid Figures

A **solid** figure is a shape that is three-dimensional, or has depth.

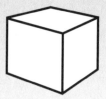

Count the shapes. Then color the graph to show how many there are of each shape.

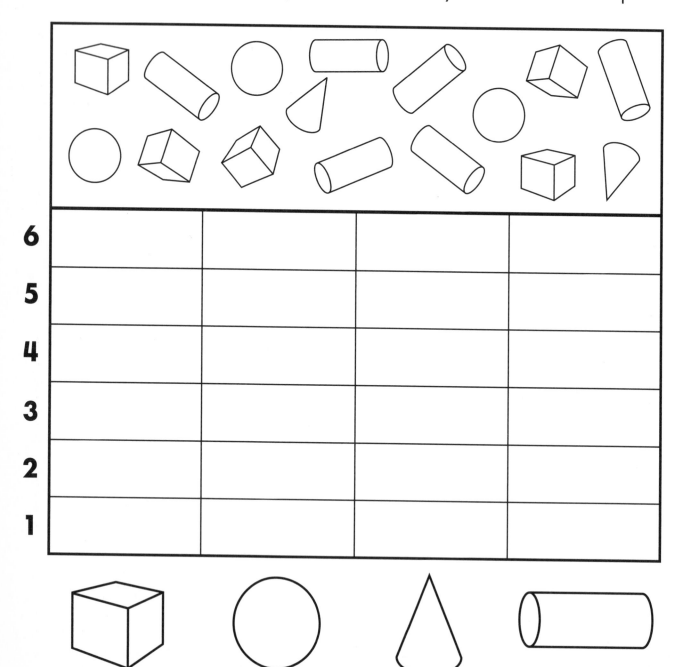

Endpoints, Line Segments, and Angles

Name____ Date____________________

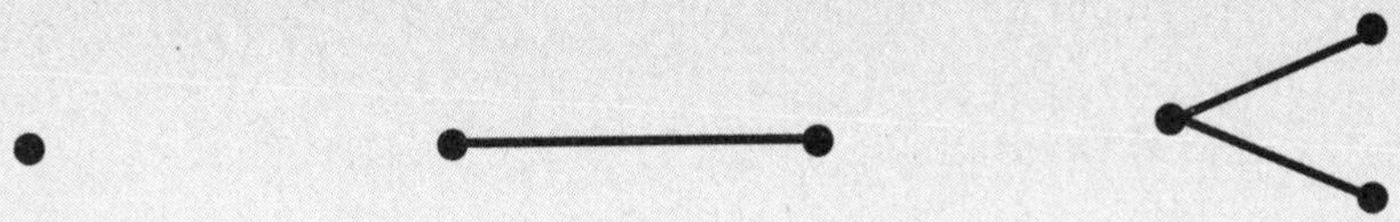

Most figures have: **endpoints, line segments,** and **angles**

Complete the chart by counting the endpoints, line segments, and angles.

	Shape		Number of Endpoints	Number of Line Segments	Number of Angles
1.	square	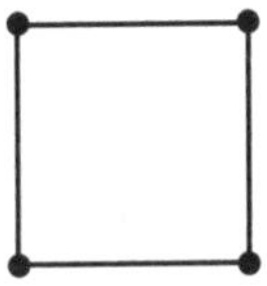			
2.	triangle	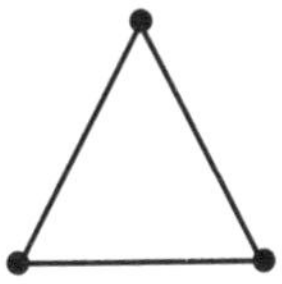			
3.	rectangle	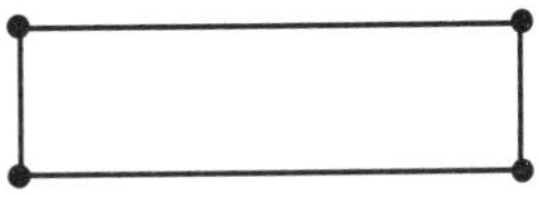			
4.	diamond	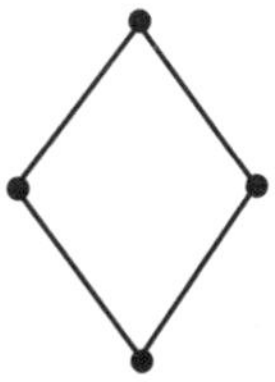			
5.	octagon	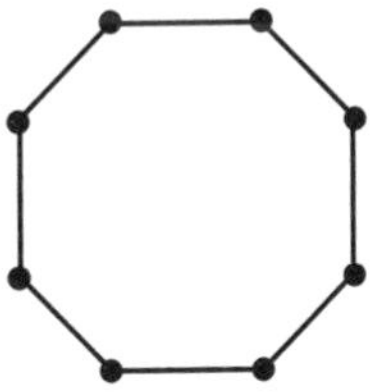			

Unit 4

Congruent Shapes

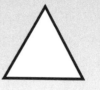

Name_____ Date_____

Congruent means the same size and shape.

Circle the correct answer.

1.
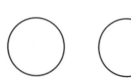

congruent

not congruent

2.

congruent

not congruent

3.

congruent

not congruent

4.

congruent

not congruent

5.

congruent

not congruent

6.
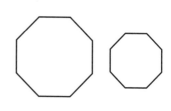

congruent

not congruent

7.

congruent

not congruent

8.

congruent

not congruent

9.
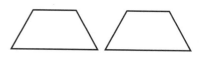

congruent

not congruent

10.

congruent

not congruent

11.

congruent

not congruent

12.

congruent

not congruent

Symmetrical Shapes

Name_____ Date_____

Symmetrical means having matching shapes on both sides of a dividing line.

Color the symmetrical shapes.

1. 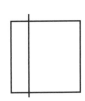	2.	3. 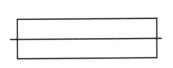
4. 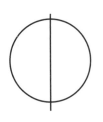	5. 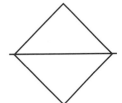	6. 
7.	8. 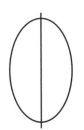	9.
10. 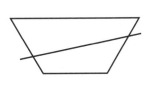	11. 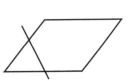	12.
13. 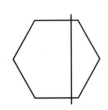	14. 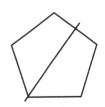	15. 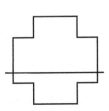

Name_____ Date_____

Perimeter is the distance around the outside of a figure.

8 in.

2 in. ☐ 2 in.

8 in.

Perimeter = 8 in. + 2 in. + 8 in. + 2 in. = 20 in.

Add the lengths of the sides to find the perimeters.

1.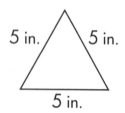
5 in. 5 in.
5 in.

_____

2.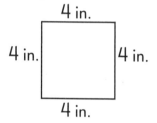
4 in.
4 in. 4 in.
4 in.

_____

3.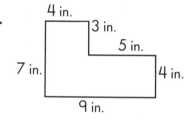
4 in.
3 in.
5 in.
7 in. 4 in.
9 in.

_____

4.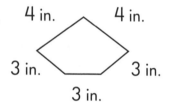
4 in. 4 in.
3 in. 3 in.
3 in.

_____

5.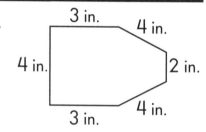
3 in.
3 in. 3 in.
3 in. 3 in.
3 in. 3 in.
3 in.

_____

6.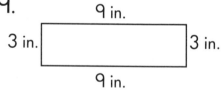
3 in.
4 in.
4 in. 2 in.
3 in. 4 in.

_____

7.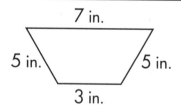
8 in.
3 in.
3 in.

_____

8.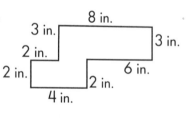
7 in.
5 in. 5 in.
3 in.

_____

9.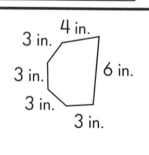
9 in.
3 in. 3 in.
9 in.

_____

10.
2 in. 2 in.
2 in. 2 in.
2 in. 2 in.
2 in. 2 in.
2 in. 2 in.

_____

11.
8 in.
3 in.
2 in. 3 in.
2 in. 6 in.
2 in.
4 in.

_____

12.
4 in.
3 in.
3 in. 6 in.
3 in.
3 in.

_____

Name_____ Date_____

Draw what comes next.

1. 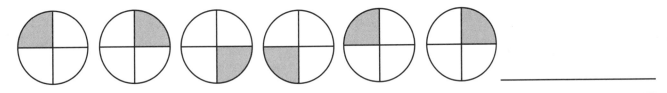 _____

2. 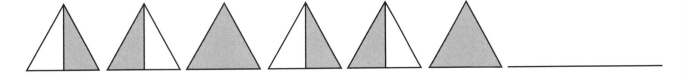 _____

3. 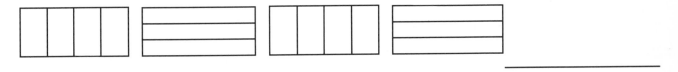 _____

4. 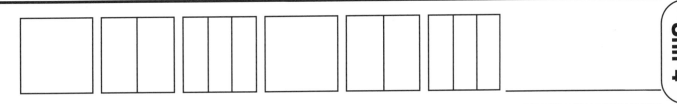 _____

5. 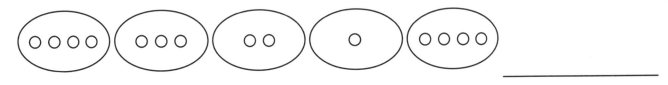 _____

6. 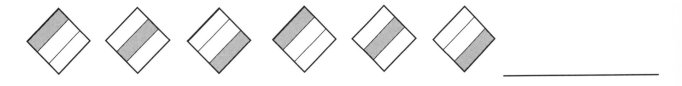 _____

7. 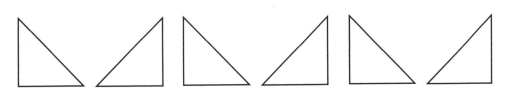 _____

Unit 4

Shape and Pattern Review

Name_____ Date_____

Fill in the circle next to the correct answer.

1.
- ○ a) square
- ○ b) sphere
- ○ c) rectangle

2. 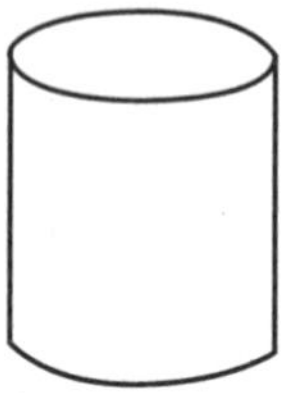
- ○ a) circle
- ○ b) sphere
- ○ c) cylinder

3. 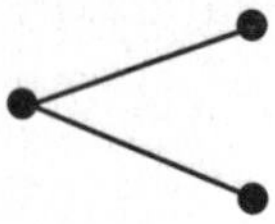
- ○ a) triangle
- ○ b) angle
- ○ c) rectangle

4. 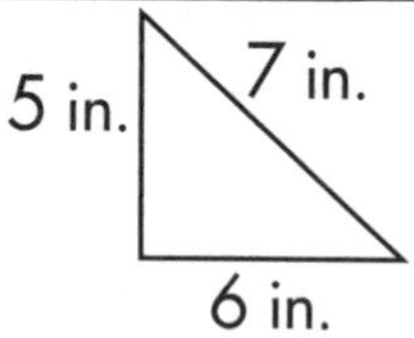 5 in. 7 in. 6 in. What is the perimeter?
- ○ a) 11 in.
- ○ b) 13 in.
- ○ c) 18 in.

5. 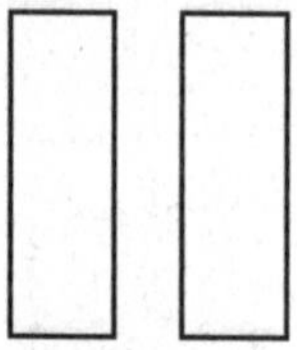
- ○ a) congruent
- ○ b) not congruent
- ○ c) symmetrical

6. 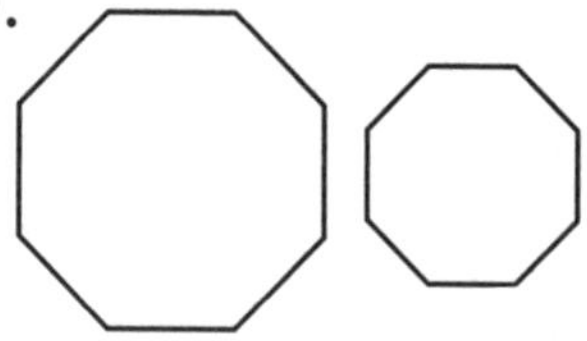
- ○ a) congruent
- ○ b) not congruent
- ○ c) symmetrical

7. 
- ○ a) symmetrical
- ○ b) not symmetrical
- ○ c) congruent

8. 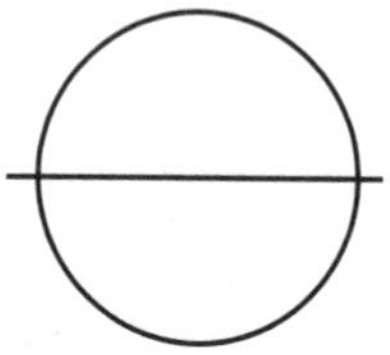
- ○ a) symmetrical
- ○ b) not symmetrical
- ○ c) congruent

9. 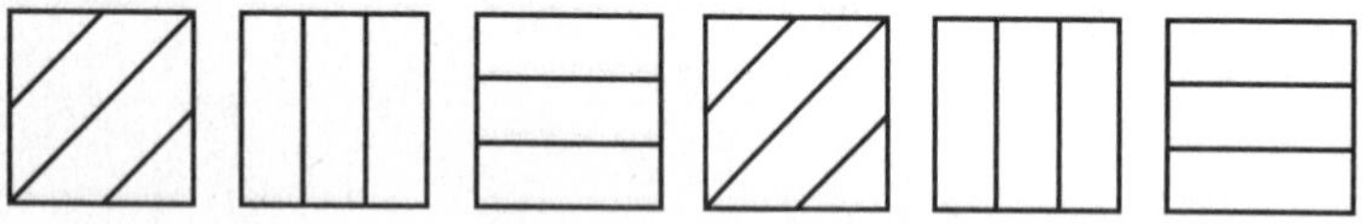
- ○ a) 
- ○ b) 
- ○ c)

10. 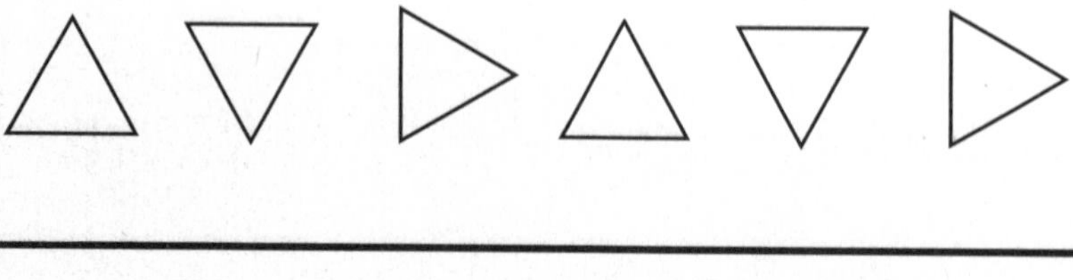
- ○ a) 
- ○ b) 
- ○ c)

Bar Graphs

Name_____ Date_____

Favorite Subject

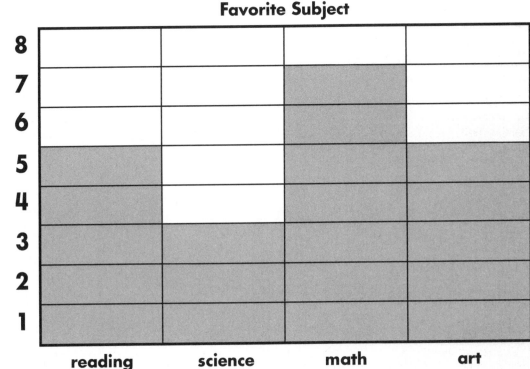

Number of Students

reading   science   math   art

Use the graph to answer the questions.

1. What was the most favorite subject? _____

2. What was the least favorite subject? _____

3. How many students named reading and science combined? _____

4. How many students named math and art combined? _____

5. How many more students said math than science? _____

6. How many students named a favorite subject? _____

Tally Marks

Name_____ Date_____

Tally marks are used
to keep count of something.
They are shown in groups of five.

Number of Soup Labels

Mrs. Jones's class	卌 卌 卌 卌 ||
Mrs. Smith's class	卌 卌 卌
Mr. Clark's class	卌 卌 卌 卌 ||||
Mrs. Patel's class	卌 卌 卌 ||||

Use the chart to answer the questions.

1. How many soup labels did Mrs. Jones's class collect? _____

2. How many soup labels did Mrs. Patel's class collect? _____

3. Which class collected the most soup labels? _____

4. Which class collected the fewest soup labels? _____

5. How many more soup labels did Mrs. Jones's class collect
   than Mrs. Smith's class? _____

6. Write your age using tally marks. _____

Name_____ Date_____

Number of Band Instruments

School		flutes	clarinets	saxophones	drums	tubas	trombones
	Ford	11	25	16	9	5	10
	Allen	14	24	20	11	7	8

Use the table to answer the questions.

1. How many trombones does Allen have? _____

2. How many flutes and clarinets does Ford have altogether? _____

3. How many more saxophones does Allen have than Ford? _____

4. Which school has the most tubas? _____

5. Which school has the fewest drums? _____

6. How many different instruments does each school have? _____

7. How many drums and trombones does Allen have altogether? _____

8. Which school has 44 clarinets and saxophones altogether? _____

9. Which school has 21 flutes and trombones altogether? _____

10. Which school has the most instruments? _____

Unit 4

Grids

Name_____ Date_____

A **grid** is a set of straight lines, labeled with numbers and letters that cross each other to show location.

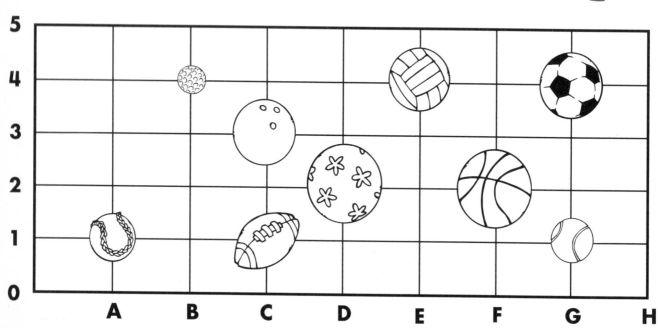

Write the location of each ball.

1. _A,1_

2.  _____

3. _____

4.  _____

5.  _____

6.  _____

7.  _____

8.  _____

9. _____

Name_____ Date_____

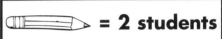
= 2 students

School Supplies

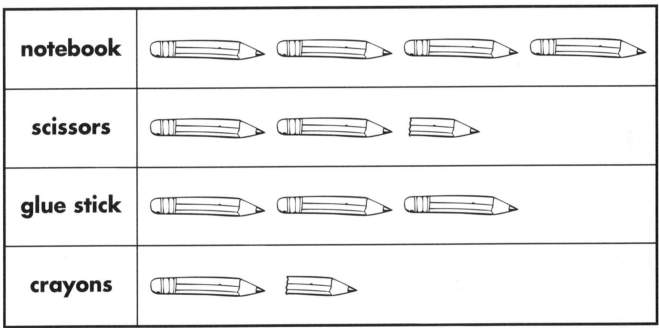

notebook	
scissors	
glue stick	
crayons	

Use the graph to answer the questions.

1. How many students bought glue sticks? _____

2. How many students bought scissors? _____

3. What did the students buy the most of? _____

4. What did the students buy the fewest of? _____

5. How many students bought school supplies? _____

Name_____ Date_____

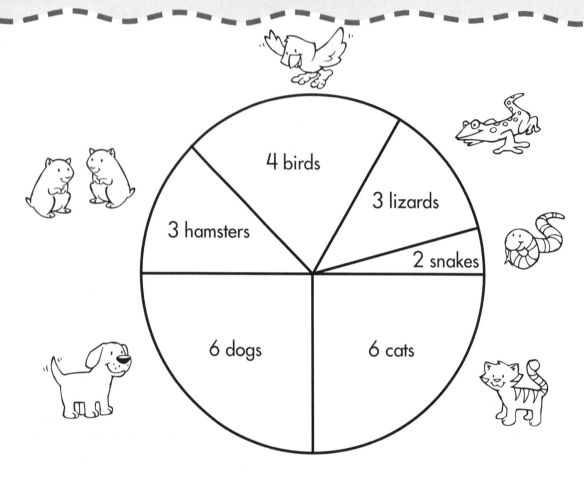

Each student named one pet. Read the graph to answer the questions.

1. How many students have a lizard? _____

2. How many students have a hamster? _____

3. How many different pets were named? _____

4. Which pet was there fewest of? _____

5. How many students have a pet? _____

6. What fraction said dogs and cats? _____

Name_____ Date_____

Show the information below on each of the graphs.

A group of students read over the holiday weekend. Here are the results:

Books Read

6 paperbacks

4 hardcovers

2 books on tape

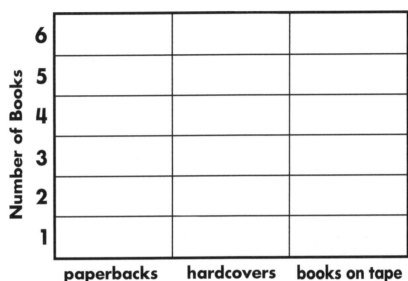

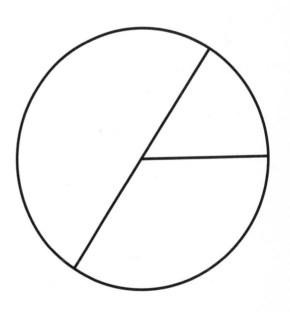

paperbacks	
hardcovers	
books on tape	

■ = one book

Unit 4

Name_____ Date_____

Show the information below on each of the graphs.

A group of students each named one favorite color.
Here are the results:

Favorite Color

Red: boys 4, girls 7
Blue: boys 8, girls 5
Yellow: boys 1, girls 3
Green: boys 6, girls 2

Use numbers to fill in the table.

	red	blue	yellow	green
boys				
girls				

Use tally marks to fill in the chart.

	red	blue	yellow	green
boys				
girls				

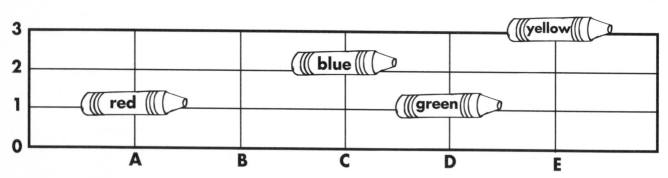

Write the location of each crayon.

red _____   blue _____

yellow _____   green _____

Name_____ Date_____

A **fraction** is part of a whole.
The top number represents part of
the whole (number of shaded parts)
and the bottom number represents
the whole (total number of parts).

$\frac{3}{4}$ =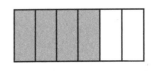

Circle the correct answer.

1.

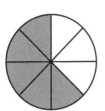

$\frac{5}{8}$ $\frac{6}{8}$

2.

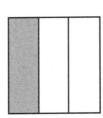

$\frac{2}{3}$ $\frac{1}{3}$

3.

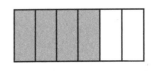

$\frac{4}{6}$ $\frac{4}{7}$

4.

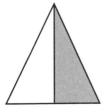

$\frac{2}{1}$ $\frac{1}{2}$

5.

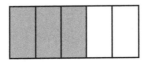

$\frac{3}{5}$ $\frac{4}{5}$

6.

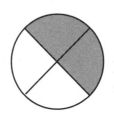

$\frac{2}{3}$ $\frac{2}{4}$

7.

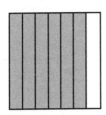

$\frac{6}{7}$ $\frac{6}{8}$

8.

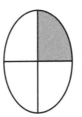

$\frac{4}{1}$ $\frac{1}{4}$

9.

$\frac{3}{8}$ $\frac{4}{8}$

Unit 4

Fractions (II)

Name_____ Date_____

Color the shape to show the fraction.

1.

$\dfrac{2}{3} =$

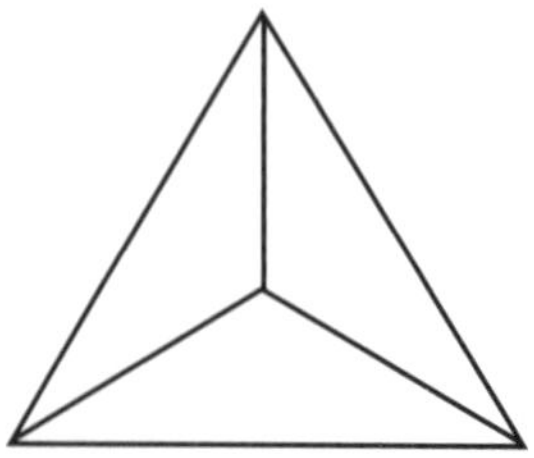

2.

$\dfrac{1}{3} =$

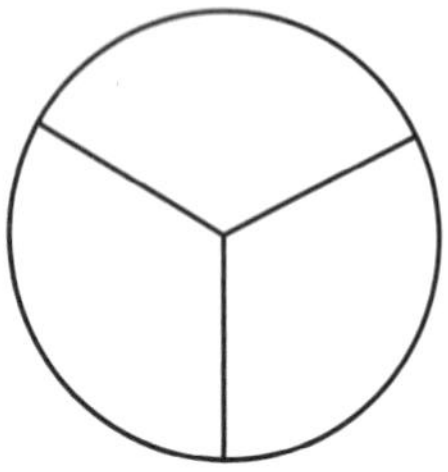

3.

$\dfrac{4}{7} =$

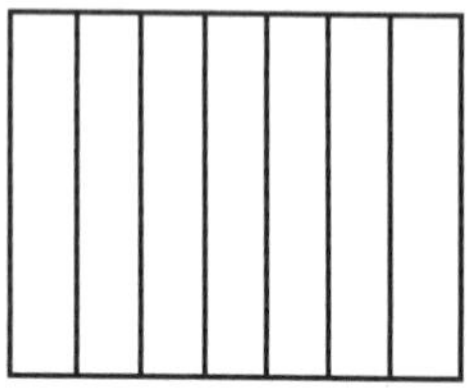

4.

$\dfrac{5}{8} =$

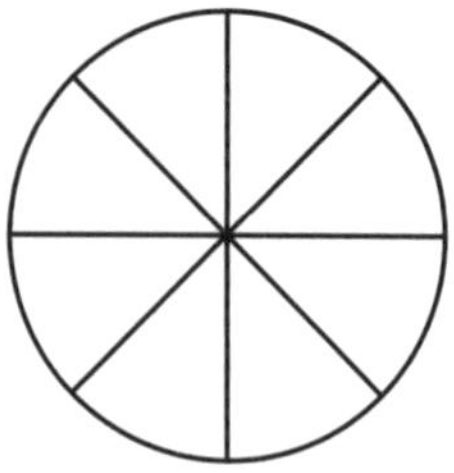

5.

$\dfrac{3}{6} =$

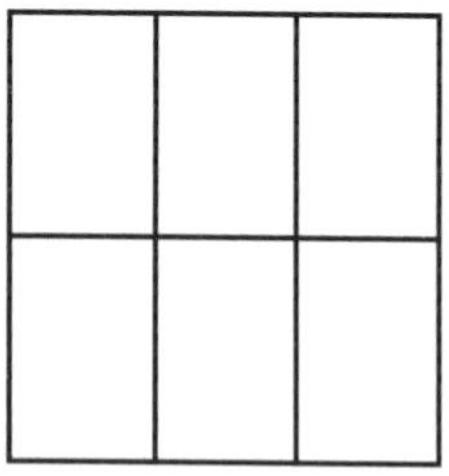

6.

$\dfrac{2}{8} =$

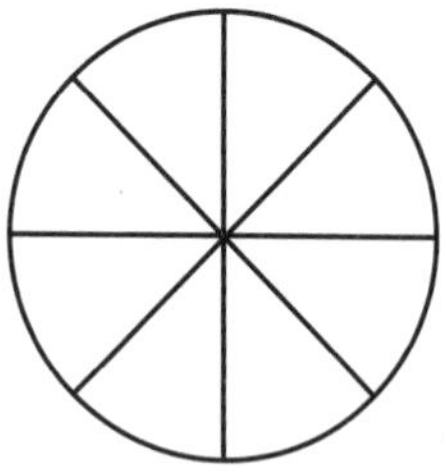

7.

$\dfrac{1}{5} =$

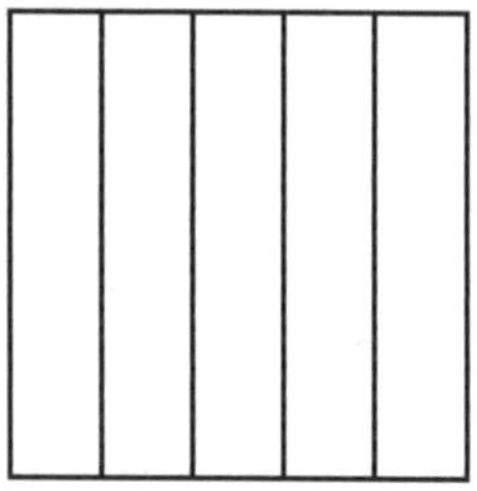

8.

$\dfrac{1}{2} =$

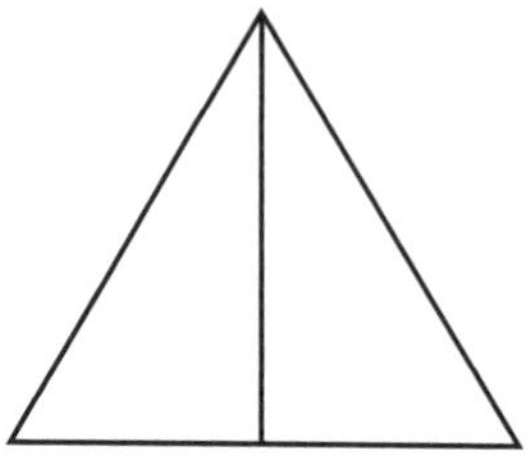

9.

$\dfrac{3}{4} =$

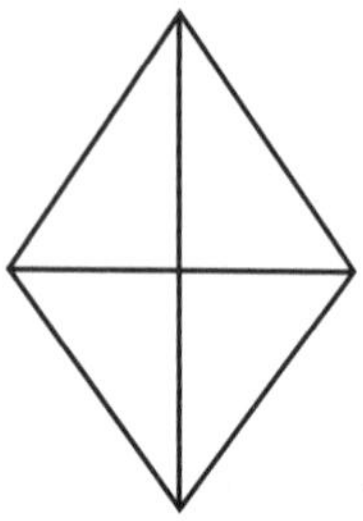

10.

$\dfrac{3}{8} =$

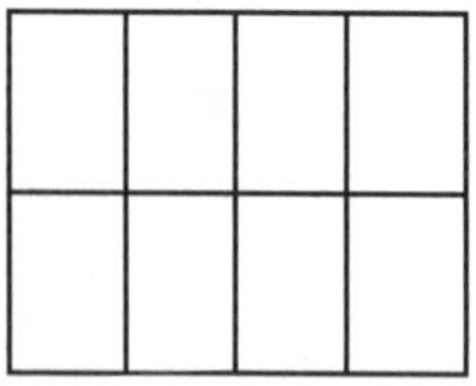

11.

$\dfrac{5}{6} =$

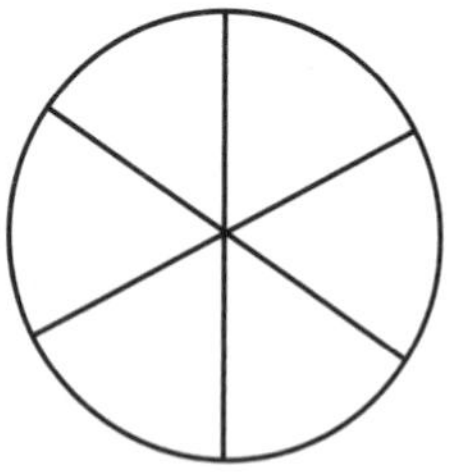

12.

$\dfrac{2}{5} =$

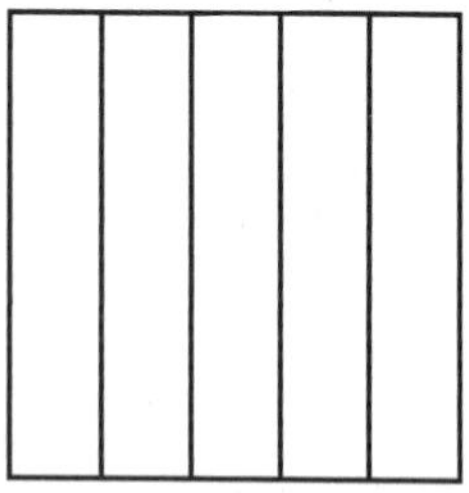

13.

$\dfrac{4}{4} =$

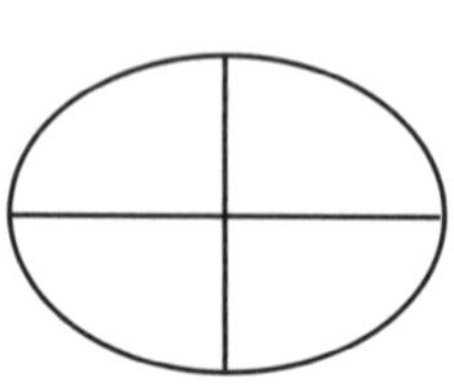

14.

$\dfrac{3}{7} =$

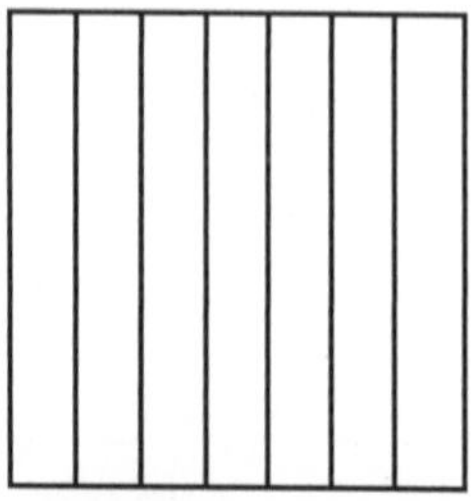

15.

$\dfrac{6}{6} =$

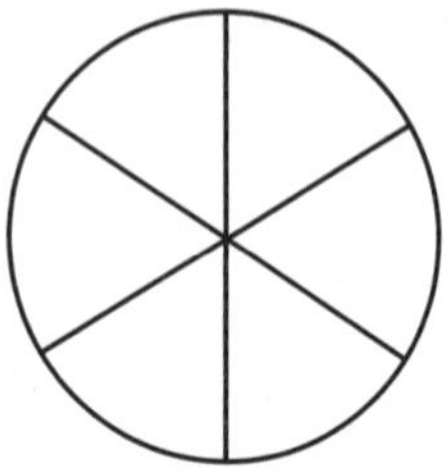

Comparing Fractions

Name_____ Date_____

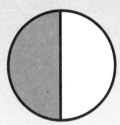 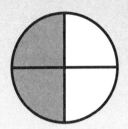

$\frac{1}{2}$ = $\frac{2}{4}$

Write **<**, **>**, or **=** to compare the fractions represented by the shapes.

1.
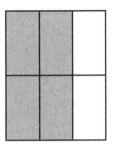 □

2.
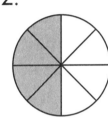 □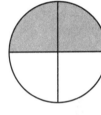

3.
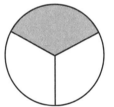 □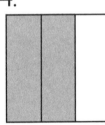

4.
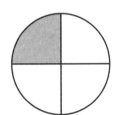 □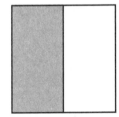

5.
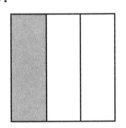 □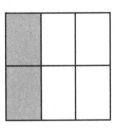

6.
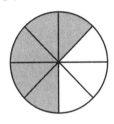 □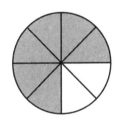

Rewrite the fractions in order from smallest to largest.

7.
$\frac{1}{4}$ $\frac{6}{8}$ $\frac{1}{6}$ $\frac{2}{3}$ $\frac{1}{2}$ _____ _____ _____ _____ _____

Name_____ Date_____

Write the fraction to show what part is shaded.

1.

_____ = 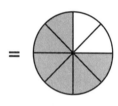   _____ = 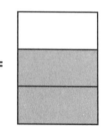   _____ =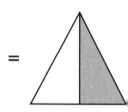

2.

_____ =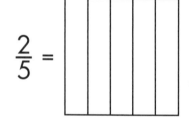

Color the shape to match the fraction.

3.

$\dfrac{2}{8}$ = $\dfrac{4}{6}$ = $\dfrac{2}{5}$ =

4.

$\dfrac{3}{4}$ = $\dfrac{1}{2}$ = $\dfrac{3}{3}$ =

Write **<**, **>**, or **=** to compare the fractions represented by the shapes.

5. □   **6.** □

Name_____ Date_____

Write the time.

1.

9:00   _____ : _____   _____ : _____

2.

_____ : _____   _____ : _____   _____ : _____

3.

_____ o'clock   _____ o'clock   _____ o'clock

4.

_____ o'clock   _____ o'clock   _____ o'clock

Unit 5

Name_____ Date_____

Write the time.

1.

7:30

____:____

____:____

2.

____:____

____:____

____:____

3.

____:____

____:____

____:____

4.

____:____

____:____

____:____

Name_____ Date_____

Circle the correct time.

1.

9:30 (10:30)　　　1:00　11:00　　　12:30　1:30

2.

7:00　8:00　　　6:00　6:30　　　3:00　3:30

3.

2:00　3:00　　　12:30　5:00　　　4:30　5:30

4.

eight-thirty　nine-thirty　　11 o'clock　12 o'clock　　8 o'clock　eight-thirty

Name_____ Date_____

It is 15 minutes after 4 o'clock.

It is 4:15.

Count by 5's to find the time. Write the time two ways.

1.

_____ minutes after _____ o'clock

_____ : _____

2.

_____ minutes after _____ o'clock

_____ : _____

3.

_____ minutes after _____ o'clock

_____ : _____

4.

_____ minutes after _____ o'clock

_____ : _____

Name_____ Date_____

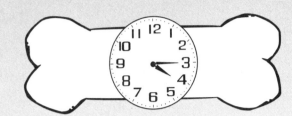

The hour hand is between 5 and 6. The minute hand is on 3. The time is 5:15.

Circle the correct time.

1.

(8:30)   9:30

12:00   1:15

5:45   5:15

2.

11:30   11:45

8:30   6:15

2:30   2:45

3.

5:30   7:30

8:45   9:30

2:30   12:15

Name_____ Date_____

Write the time.

1.

9:45   ___:___   ___:___

2.

___:___   ___:___   ___:___

3.

___:___   ___:___   ___:___

4.

___:___   ___:___   ___:___

Name_____ Date_____

Draw a line from each clock to the matching time.

7:15

7:45

3:45

2:45

4:15

6:15

1:15

5:45

Name_____ Date_____

Draw hands on each clock to show the time.

1.

6:45

3:15

12:45

2.

7:15

9:45

2:15

3.

8:45

4:15

1:45

4.

5:15

10:45

11:15

Name_____ Date_____

It is 10 minutes after 7 o'clock.
It is 7:10.

There are 60 minutes in 1 hour.

Count by 5's. Write the numbers around the clock.

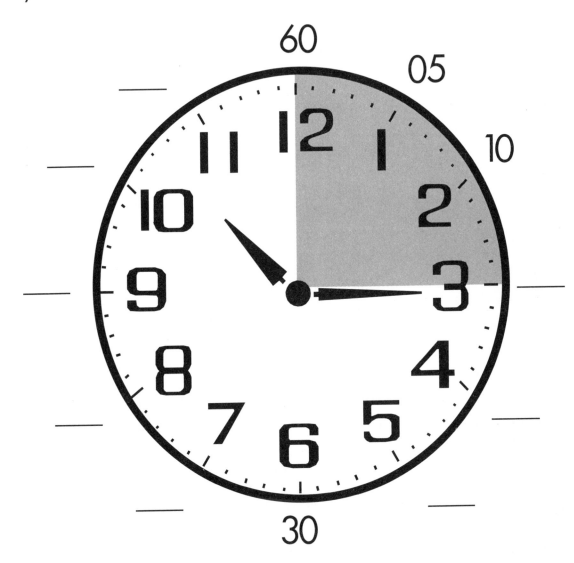

Time: Five-Minute Intervals (II)

Name_____ Date_____

It is 4:20.

"I'm late!"

Circle the correct time.

1.

1:10

1:15

2.

3:15

3:40

3.

9:35

9:20

4.

2:45

2:05

5.

7:35

7:20

6.

1:10

10:55

7.

6:50

6:15

8.

8:30

8:25

Name_____ Date_____

Write the time.

1.

10:20 _____

___ : ___

___ : ___

2.

___ : ___

___ : ___

___ : ___

3.

___ : ___

___ : ___

___ : ___

4.

___ : ___

___ : ___

___ : ___

Unit 5

Name_____ Date_____

Draw hands on each clock to show the time.

1.

6:40

3:10

12:50

2.

5:05

8:25

2:15

3.

1:20

4:55

7:35

4.

9:30

11:45

10:10

Name_____ Date_____

Both clocks show 9:20.

Draw a line from each clock to the matching time.

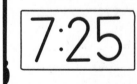

8:05

5:50

2:35

7:25

10:15

Time: a.m. and p.m.

Name_____ Date_____

a.m. indicates the time between midnight and noon.

p.m. indicates the time between noon and midnight

Read each statement. Circle **a.m.** or **p.m.** to show the time of day.

1. Billy eats breakfast at 6:45 in the morning.   a.m.   p.m.

2. Debbie practices her violin every afternoon at 3:30.   a.m.   p.m.

3. Larry watches cartoons before school.   a.m.   p.m.

4. Bob arrives home from school at 3:25 each afternoon.   a.m.   p.m.

5. Kathy does her homework every afternoon at 4:15.   a.m.   p.m.

6. Helen wakes up at 6:00 each morning.   a.m.   p.m.

7. David sets the table for dinner every evening at 6:00.   a.m.   p.m.

Time: Daily Routines

Look at the pictures and write the time you do each activity. Then draw hands on each clock to show the time.

1.

_____ : _____

2.

_____ : _____

3.

_____ : _____

4.

_____ : _____

5.

_____ : _____

6.

_____ : _____

Unit 5

Elapsed Time

Name_____   Date_____

Now it is 4:00.

30 minutes later it will be 4:30.

Draw clock hands to show the time **30 minutes later**. Write the time.

Now   30 minutes later

1.

_____ : _____

2.
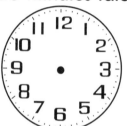

_____ : _____

3.

_____ : _____

4.

_____ : _____

Time Word Problems

Name_____ Date_____

Read each problem. Write the answer.

1. Kristen woke up at 9:00. She left for the museum 30 minutes later. What time did Kristen leave for the museum?

_____ : _____

2. Brad got to the museum at 10:20. Pat got to the museum 25 minutes later. What time did Pat get to the museum?

_____ : _____

3. Lindsay got to the museum at 1:00. She went home 3 hours later. What time did Lindsay go home?

_____ : _____

4. The dinosaur show starts at 2:15. It lasts 30 minutes. What time does the dinosaur show end?

_____ : _____

5. The bus arrives at 3:00. The museum is 35 minutes from Joey's house. What time will Joey get home?

_____ : _____

Time Practice

○ a) 7:10
● b) 8:10
○ c) 9:00

Fill in the circle next to the correct time.

1.

○ a) 7:05
○ b) 9:05
○ c) 9:10

2.

○ a) 7:25
○ b) 7:30
○ c) 7:35

3.

○ a) 3:20
○ b) 3:40
○ c) 3:45

4.

○ a) 4:15
○ b) 4:30
○ c) 5:30

5.

○ a) 11:15
○ b) 11:20
○ c) 11:45

6.

○ a) 4:00
○ b) 5:00
○ c) 6:00

7.

○ a) 10:55
○ b) 11:00
○ c) 11:50

8.

○ a) 9:00
○ b) 1:15
○ c) 2:45

Name_____ Date_____

NOVEMBER

Sunday	Monday	Tuesday	Wednesday	Thursday	Friday	Saturday
				1	2	3
4	5	6 Election Day	7	8	9	10 Football Game
11	12	13	14	15	16	17
18	19 School Play	20	21	22 Thanksgiving	23	24
25	26	27	28	29	30	

Use the calendar to answer the questions.

1. What month is shown above? _____

2. How many days are in this month? _____

3. Which day of the week is the first day of this month? _____

4. How many Tuesdays are in this month? _____

5. How many days in a week? _____

6. What day of the week is Thanksgiving? _____

7. What is the date of the football game? _____

8. What is the date of the school play? _____

9. What day of the week is Election Day? _____

10. What month comes after this month? _____

Name_____ Date_____

Use a ruler to measure the pencils in inches or centimeters.

1.

_____cm.

2.

_____in.

3.

_____cm.

4.

_____in.

5.

_____cm.

6.

_____in.

7.

_____cm.

Measurement: Pounds

Name_____ Date_____

This box of spaghetti weighs **1 pound**.

Fill in the circle next to the correct answer.

1.

   ○ a) < 1 pound

   ○ b) > 1 pound

2.

   ○ a) < 1 pound

   ○ b) > 1 pound

3.

   ○ a) < 1 pound

   ○ b) > 1 pound

4.

   ○ a) < 1 pound

   ○ b) > 1 pound

5.

   ○ a) < 1 pound

   ○ b) > 1 pound

6.

   ○ a) < 1 pound

   ○ b) > 1 pound

7.

   ○ a) < 1 pound

   ○ b) > 1 pound

8.

   ○ a) < 1 pound

   ○ b) > 1 pound

9.

   ○ a) < 1 pound

   ○ b) > 1 pound

Name_____ Date_____

These bananas weigh **1 kilogram**.

Fill in the circle next to the correct answer.

1.

○ a) < 1 kilogram
○ b) > 1 kilogram

2.

○ a) < 1 kilogram
○ b) > 1 kilogram

3.

○ a) < 1 kilogram
○ b) > 1 kilogram

4.

○ a) < 1 kilogram
○ b) > 1 kilogram

5.

○ a) < 1 kilogram
○ b) > 1 kilogram

6.

○ a) < 1 kilogram
○ b) > 1 kilogram

7.

○ a) < 1 kilogram
○ b) > 1 kilogram

8.

○ a) < 1 kilogram
○ b) > 1 kilram

9.

○ a) < 1 kilogram
○ b) > 1 kilogram

Measurement: Cups, Pints, and Quarts

Name_____ Date_____

1 cup   **2 cups = 1 pint**   **4 cups = 1 quart**

Color the cups to show the same amonts.

1.

2.

3.

4.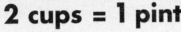

5.

© Learning Horizons

Measurement: Liters

 less than 1 liter  1 liter  more than 1 liter

Fill in the circle next to the correct answer.

1.

○ a) < 1 liter

○ b) > 1 liter

2.

○ a) < 1 liter

○ b) > 1 liter

3.

○ a) < 1 liter

○ b) > 1 liter

4.

○ a) < 1 liter

○ b) > 1 liter

5.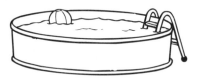

○ a) < 1 liter

○ b) > 1 liter

6.

○ a) < 1 liter

○ b) > 1 liter

7.

○ a) < 1 liter

○ b) > 1 liter

8.

○ a) < 1 liter

○ b) > 1 liter

9.

○ a) < 1 liter

○ b) > 1 liter

Name_____ Date_____

Circle the correct temperature.

1.

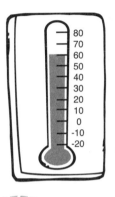 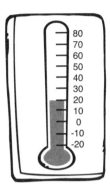 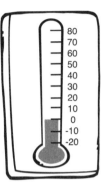 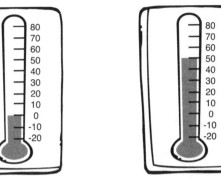

(60°)   80°   10°   20°   0°   10°   50°   60°

2.

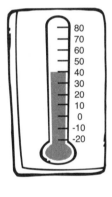 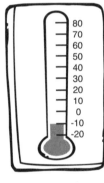 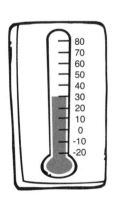 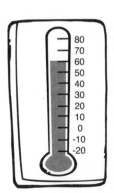

40°   50°   -10°   10°   70°   80°   20°   30°

Write the correct temperature.

3.

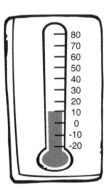 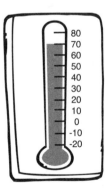

○   ○   ○   ○

_____   _____   _____   _____

Name_____ Date_____

Write the length.

1.

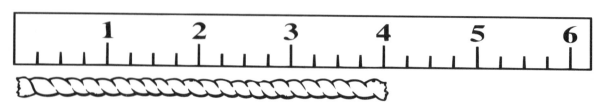

about _____ inches

2.

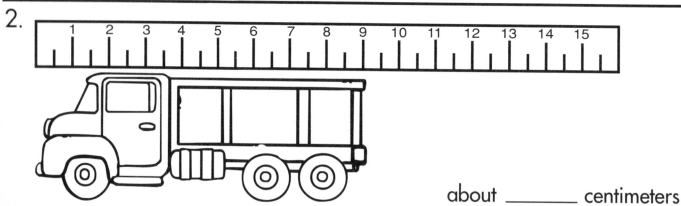

about _____ centimeters

Color the cups to show the same amount.

3.

Fill in the circle of the correct answer.

4.

⊙ a) < 1 pound

⊙ b) > 1 pound

5.

⊙ a) < 1 kilogram

⊙ b) > 1 kilogram

Multiplication: Repeated Groups (1)

Name_____ Date_____

The **multiplication sign (x)** means groups of.

2 x 5 = 2 groups of 5 = ☆☆☆☆☆ + ☆☆☆☆☆ = 10

Write the letter for the correct answer.

1. 4 x 2 = _____

2. 1 x 5 = _____

3. 2 x 3 = _____

4. 5 x 2 = _____

5. 3 x 1 = _____

6. 3 x 4 = _____

7. 4 x 1 = _____

8. 2 x 2 = _____

a) 🐢🐢🐢 🐢🐢

b) 🐢🐢 🐢🐢 🐢🐢
   🐢🐢 🐢🐢 🐢🐢

c) 🐢 🐢
   🐢 🐢

d) 🐢 🐢 🐢 🐢
   🐢 🐢 🐢 🐢

e) 🐢 🐢 🐢 🐢

f) 🐢🐢🐢
   🐢🐢🐢

g) 🐢 🐢 🐢

h)  🐢 🐢 🐢 🐢 🐢
   🐢 🐢 🐢 🐢 🐢

Name_____ Date_____

Each bug has the same number of spots. Count or multiply to find how many spots in all.

Each one of us has 2 spots.

4 ladybugs x 2 spots on each = 8 spots

Find how many spots by counting or multiplying. Color all the spots.

1.

_____3_____ frogs

x _____4_____ spots on each

_____12_____ spots in all

2.

_____ dogs

x _____ spots on each

_____ spots in all

3.

_____ cats

x _____ spots on each

_____ spots in all

4.

_____ mushrooms

x _____ spots on each

_____ spots in all

Name_____ Date_____

There are 3 rows of daisies.
There are 5 daisies in each row.
There are 15 daisies in all.

Count how many rows. Count how many in each row. Write the total. Then find how many by multiplying.

1.

2 rows of 4 = _____ s

2 x 4 = _____

2.

3 rows of 3 = _____ s

3 x 3 = _____

3.

3 rows of 4 = _____ s

3 x 4 = _____

4.

2 rows of 5 = _____ s

2 x 5 = _____

5.

3 rows of 6 = _____ s

3 x 6 = _____

6.

4 rows of 5 = _____ s

4 x 5 = _____

Unit 6

Name_____ Date_____

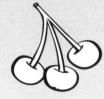

How many cherries?
Add or multiply to find out.

4 groups of 3
3 + 3 + 3 + 3 = 12
3 × 4 = 12

Find how many pieces of fruit by adding. Then find how many by multiplying.

1.

2 groups of 3   3 + 3 = _____   2 × 3 = _____

2.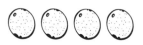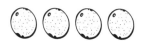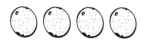

4 groups of 4   4 + 4 + 4 + 4 = _____   4 × 4 = _____

3.

2 groups of 5   5 + 5 = _____   2 × 5 = _____

4.

3 groups of 3   3 + 3 + 3 = _____   3 × 3 = _____

5.

3 groups of 4   4 + 4 + 4 = _____   3 × 4 = _____

Name_____ Date_____

Draw groups to show the multiplication problem. Then add the groups together and write the answer.

1. $2 \times 2 =$ ○ ○ $=$ $2 + 2$ $=$ $\boxed{4}$
   ○ ○

2. $4 \times 1 =$ $=$ $=$ $\boxed{}$

3. $4 \times 3 =$ $=$ $=$ $\boxed{}$

4. $1 \times 5 =$ $=$ $=$ $\boxed{}$

5. $6 \times 1 =$ $=$ $=$ $\boxed{}$

6. $3 \times 5 =$ $=$ $=$ $\boxed{}$

7. $4 \times 2 =$ $=$ $=$ $\boxed{}$

8. $1 \times 3 =$ $=$ $=$ $\boxed{}$

Unit 6

Name_____ Date_____

Any number multiplied by zero equals zero.
Zero multiplied by any other number
will also equal zero.

3 x 0 = 3 added 0 times = 0 (because there are no 3's)
0 x 3 = 0 added 3 times = 0 + 0 + 0 = 0

Multiply.

1.
```
    1        0        6        3        0
  x 0      x 4      x 0      x 0      x 7
```

2.
```
    5        7        0        9        2
  x 0      x 0      x 8      x 0      x 0
```

3.
```
   26       18       42       65       50
  x 0      x 0      x 0      x 0      x 0
```

4.
```
   21       30       53       67       42
  x 0      x 0      x 0      x 0      x 0
```

Name_____ Date_____

A number multiplied by one equals itself.
One multiplied by any other number
equals that number.

3 x 1 = 3 added 1 time = 3
1 x 3 = 1 added 3 times = 1 + 1 + 1 = 3

Multiply.

1.
$$\begin{array}{r} 8 \\ \times\ 1 \\ \hline \end{array}$$
$$\begin{array}{r} 1 \\ \times\ 5 \\ \hline \end{array}$$
$$\begin{array}{r} 6 \\ \times\ 1 \\ \hline \end{array}$$
$$\begin{array}{r} 3 \\ \times\ 1 \\ \hline \end{array}$$
$$\begin{array}{r} 1 \\ \times\ 7 \\ \hline \end{array}$$

2.
$$\begin{array}{r} 9 \\ \times\ 1 \\ \hline \end{array}$$
$$\begin{array}{r} 1 \\ \times\ 2 \\ \hline \end{array}$$
$$\begin{array}{r} 1 \\ \times\ 4 \\ \hline \end{array}$$
$$\begin{array}{r} 7 \\ \times\ 1 \\ \hline \end{array}$$
$$\begin{array}{r} 2 \\ \times\ 1 \\ \hline \end{array}$$

3.
$$\begin{array}{r} 46 \\ \times\ 1 \\ \hline \end{array}$$
$$\begin{array}{r} 28 \\ \times\ 1 \\ \hline \end{array}$$
$$\begin{array}{r} 44 \\ \times\ 1 \\ \hline \end{array}$$
$$\begin{array}{r} 68 \\ \times\ 1 \\ \hline \end{array}$$
$$\begin{array}{r} 73 \\ \times\ 1 \\ \hline \end{array}$$

4.
$$\begin{array}{r} 29 \\ \times\ 1 \\ \hline \end{array}$$
$$\begin{array}{r} 33 \\ \times\ 1 \\ \hline \end{array}$$
$$\begin{array}{r} 55 \\ \times\ 1 \\ \hline \end{array}$$
$$\begin{array}{r} 99 \\ \times\ 1 \\ \hline \end{array}$$
$$\begin{array}{r} 82 \\ \times\ 1 \\ \hline \end{array}$$

Unit 6

Multiplication: With 2

The domino has two sides.
Each side has 3 dots.
How many dots in all?

2 groups of 3 dots
2 x 3 = 6
6 dots in all

Multiply to find the total number of dots.

1. _____ groups of _____ dots

   _____ x _____

   _____ dots in all

2. _____ groups of _____ dots

   _____ x _____

   _____ dots in all

3. _____ groups of _____ dots

   _____ x _____

   _____ dots in all

4. _____ groups of _____ dots

   _____ x _____

   _____ dots in all

5. _____ groups of _____ dots

   _____ x _____

   _____ dots in all

6. _____ groups of _____ dots

   _____ x _____

   _____ dots in all

Name_____ Date_____

There are three scoops of ice cream.
Each scoop has three chocolate chips.
How many choclate chips in all?

3 groups of 3 chocolate chips = 3 x 3 = 9

Multiply to find the total number of chocolate chips.

1.

_____ groups of _____ chips

_____ x _____

_____ chips in all

2.

_____ groups of _____ chips

_____ x _____

_____ chips in all

3.

_____ groups of _____ chips

_____ x _____

_____ chips in all

4.

_____ groups of _____ chips

_____ x _____

_____ chips in all

5.

_____ groups of _____ chips

_____ x _____

_____ chips in all

6.

_____ groups of _____ chips

_____ x _____

_____ chips in all

Unit 6

Multiplication Word Problems (1)

Name_____ Date_____

Remember, with equal groups you can multiply.

On Monday, 3 bunnies got mail.
Each bunny got 2 letters.
How many letters in all?

3 groups of 2
3 x 2 = 6
6 letters in all

$$\begin{array}{r} 3 \\ \underline{\times\ 2} \\ 6 \end{array}$$

Read each problem. Multiply to find the answer.

1. On Tuesday, 3 bunnies got mail.
   Each bunny got 3 letters.
   How many letters in all?   _____

2. On Wednesday, 3 bunnies got mail.
   Each bunny got 1 letter.
   How many letters in all?   _____

3. On Thursday, 2 bunnies got mail.
   Each bunny got 2 letters.
   How many letters in all?   _____

4. On Friday, 2 bunnies got mail.
   Each bunny got 3 letters.
   How many letters in all?   _____

5. On Saturday, 1 bunny got mail.
   The bunny got 3 letters.
   How many letters in all?   _____

Multiplication Word Problems (II)

Name_____ Date_____

Read each problem. Write a number sentence and solve.

1. Each roller coaster car holds 3 people. How many people are seated in 2 cars?

   _____

2. A game has 3 fish in each fishbowl. How many fish in 4 fishbowls?

   _____

3. The Tilt-a-Whirl costs 5 tickets to ride. How many tickets for 3 people to ride?

   _____

4. Railroad cars hold 6 people each. How many people can ride in 2 railroad cars?

   _____

5. A theme park visor costs $6. Mary's family buys 3 visors. How much do they spend?

   _____

6. There are 2 clowns walking around the park. Each clown holds 4 balloons. How many balloons in all?

   _____

Name_____ Date_____

Draw lines to match.

2 groups of 3

3 groups of 4

2 groups of 5

3 groups of 3

3 groups of 5

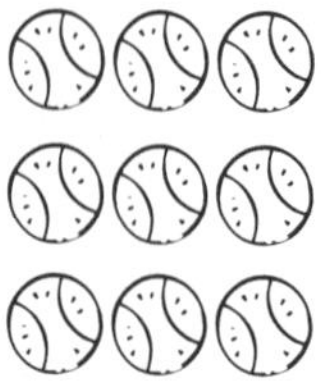

2 groups of 7

$5 + 5$	2×3	12
$3 + 3$	3×4	9
$7 + 7$	2×7	6
$3 + 3 + 3$	3×5	10
$4 + 4 + 4$	3×3	14
$5 + 5 + 5$	2×5	15

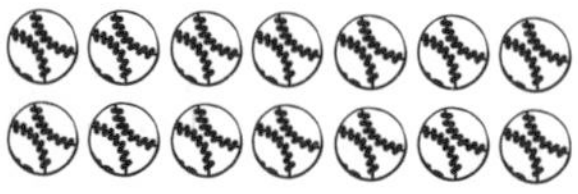

Name_____ Date_____

Fill in the circle next to the correct answer.

1.
$$\begin{array}{r} 96 \\ -\ 54 \\ \hline \end{array}$$
○ a) 41
○ b) 42
○ c) 45

2.
$$\begin{array}{r} 75 \\ +\ 14 \\ \hline \end{array}$$
○ a) 83
○ b) 86
○ c) 89

3.
$$\begin{array}{r} 25 \\ +\ 26 \\ \hline \end{array}$$
○ a) 51
○ b) 56
○ c) 61

4.
$$\begin{array}{r} 68 \\ +\ 14 \\ \hline \end{array}$$
○ a) 72
○ b) 82
○ c) 92

5.
$$\begin{array}{r} 96 \\ -\ 58 \\ \hline \end{array}$$
○ a) 38
○ b) 48
○ c) 58

6.
$$\begin{array}{r} 57 \\ -\ 29 \\ \hline \end{array}$$
○ a) 15
○ b) 18
○ c) 28

7.
$$\begin{array}{r} 66 \\ +\ 24 \\ \hline \end{array}$$
○ a) 80
○ b) 90
○ c) 95

8.
$$\begin{array}{r} 80 \\ -\ 38 \\ \hline \end{array}$$
○ a) 42
○ b) 44
○ c) 48

9.
$$\begin{array}{r} 27 \\ -\ 17 \\ \hline \end{array}$$
○ a) 7
○ b) 20
○ c) 10

10.
$$\begin{array}{r} 45 \\ +\ 45 \\ \hline \end{array}$$
○ a) 80
○ b) 90
○ c) 95

11.
$$\begin{array}{r} 84 \\ -\ 17 \\ \hline \end{array}$$
○ a) 67
○ b) 76
○ c) 86

12.
$$\begin{array}{r} 33 \\ +\ 20 \\ \hline \end{array}$$
○ a) 13
○ b) 53
○ c) 63

Unit 7

Practice Test: Place Value

Name_____ Date_____

Fill in the circle next to the correct answer.

1.

400 + 70 + 2

- ○ a) 427
- ○ b) 422
- ○ c) 472

2.

800 + 30 + 9

- ○ a) 839
- ○ b) 399
- ○ c) 893

3.

100 + 50 + 6

- ○ a) 516
- ○ b) 156
- ○ c) 165

4.

500 + 80 + 3

- ○ a) 538
- ○ b) 583
- ○ c) 883

5.

358

- ○ a) 300 + 50 + 8
- ○ b) 400 + 20 + 8
- ○ c) 500 + 30 + 8

6.

226

- ○ a) 600 + 20 + 2
- ○ b) 200 + 60 + 2
- ○ c) 200 + 20 + 6

7.

697

- ○ a) 700 + 90 + 7
- ○ b) 600 + 90 + 7
- ○ c) 600 + 70 + 9

8.

791

- ○ a) 700 + 90 + 1
- ○ b) 900 + 90 + 7
- ○ c) 700 + 10 + 9

9.

9 hundreds,
2 tens, 5 ones

- ○ a) 259
- ○ b) 529
- ○ c) 925

10.

3 hundreds,
8 tens, 1 one

- ○ a) 538
- ○ b) 381
- ○ c) 451

11.

8 hundreds,
7 tens, 6 ones

- ○ a) 876
- ○ b) 768
- ○ c) 678

12.

6 hundreds,
4 tens, 7 ones

- ○ a) 467
- ○ b) 647
- ○ c) 732

Practice Test: Number Order

Name_____ Date_____

Fill in the circle next to the correct answer.

1. What comes before 776?	○ a) 775 ○ b) 777 ○ c) 800
2. What comes between 411 and 413?	○ a) 380 ○ b) 400 ○ c) 412
3. What comes after 599?	○ a) 600 ○ b) 580 ○ c) 595
4. What comes before 500?	○ a) 469 ○ b) 519 ○ c) 499
5. What comes after 639?	○ a) 600 ○ b) 580 ○ c) 640
6. fifty-one, fifty-two, ____	○ a) 53 ○ b) 40 ○ c) 499
7. twelve, ____, fourteen	○ a) 12 ○ b) 13 ○ c) 18
8. 237 ☐ 327	○ a) > ○ b) < ○ c) =
9. 60 ☐ 59	○ a) > ○ b) < ○ c) =
10. 89 ☐ 86	○ a) > ○ b) < ○ c) =
11. ☐ ☐ ☐ ☐	○ a) first ○ b) second ○ c) third
12. ↓ ☐ ☐ ☐ ☐	○ a) first ○ b) fourth ○ c) third

Unit 7

Practice Test: Number Patterns

Name_____ Date_____

Fill in the circle next to the correct answer.

1.

25, 30, 35, _____

- ○ a) 45
- ○ b) 15
- ○ c) 40

2.

60, 70, 80, _____

- ○ a) 90
- ○ b) 80
- ○ c) 50

3.

28, 30, 32, _____

- ○ a) 36
- ○ b) 34
- ○ c) 26

4.

9, 12, 15, _____

- ○ a) 18
- ○ b) 21
- ○ c) 6

5.

34, 36, 38, _____

- ○ a) 37
- ○ b) 39
- ○ c) 40

6.

80, 85, 90, _____

- ○ a) 76
- ○ b) 95
- ○ c) 100

7.

144, 145, 146, _____

- ○ a) 147
- ○ b) 149
- ○ c) 150

8.

722, 724, 726, _____

- ○ a) 700
- ○ b) 727
- ○ c) 728

9.

700, 710, 720, _____

- ○ a) 725
- ○ b) 730
- ○ c) 740

10.

553, 556, 559, _____

- ○ a) 562
- ○ b) 560
- ○ c) 555

11.

255, 260, 265, _____

- ○ a) 275
- ○ b) 280
- ○ c) 270

12.

440, 442, 444, _____

- ○ a) 448
- ○ b) 446
- ○ c) 447

Practice Test: Addition and Subtraction (II)

Name_____ Date_____

Fill in the circle next to the correct answer.

1.
$$253 + 221$$
- ○ a) 474
- ○ b) 442
- ○ c) 456

2.
$$578 - 246$$
- ○ a) 421
- ○ b) 312
- ○ c) 332

3.
$$625 + 126$$
- ○ a) 651
- ○ b) 751
- ○ c) 641

4.
$$455 + 417$$
- ○ a) 872
- ○ b) 882
- ○ c) 992

5.
$$987 - 127$$
- ○ a) 764
- ○ b) 760
- ○ c) 860

6.
$$357 - 111$$
- ○ a) 246
- ○ b) 218
- ○ c) 228

7.
$$405 + 166$$
- ○ a) 569
- ○ b) 571
- ○ c) 301

8.
$$882 - 171$$
- ○ a) 611
- ○ b) 711
- ○ c) 811

9.
$$632 - 318$$
- ○ a) 214
- ○ b) 413
- ○ c) 314

10.
$$144 + 144$$
- ○ a) 288
- ○ b) 348
- ○ c) 188

11.
$$440 + 67$$
- ○ a) 507
- ○ b) 570
- ○ c) 467

12.
$$700 - 500$$
- ○ a) 100
- ○ b) 200
- ○ c) 300

Unit 7

Practice Test: Word Problems

Name_____ Date_____

Fill in the circle next to the correct answer.

1. Ken had 53 pieces of candy.
   He gave 28 of them away.
   How many pieces of candy does
   Ken have left?

   ○ a) 15
   ○ b) 25
   ○ c) 28

2. Tom has 47 quarters.
   His dad gave him 14 more.
   How many quarters does Tom
   have in all?

   ○ a) 61
   ○ b) 51
   ○ c) 33

3. Tina read 433 pages of her book.
   If there are 873 total pages, how many
   more pages does she have left to read?

   ○ a) 230
   ○ b) 400
   ○ c) 440

4. John saw 230 ants while on a picnic.
   He dropped a cookie and then 119 more
   ants came out. How many ants did John
   see altogether?

   ○ a) 345
   ○ b) 349
   ○ c) 394

5. Eric had 167 hats.
   His uncle gave him 82 more.
   How many hats does Eric have in all?

   ○ a) 115
   ○ b) 125
   ○ c) 249

6. Michelle had 377 candles.
   She used 240 of them.
   How many candles does she have left?

   ○ a) 137
   ○ b) 117
   ○ c) 501

Name_____ Date_____

Fill in the circle next to the correct answer.

1.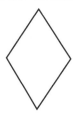
- ○ a) square
- ○ b) triangle
- ○ c) diamond

2. 9 in.
2 in. [rectangle] 2 in.
9 in.
What is the perimeter?
- ○ a) 20 in.
- ○ b) 22 in.
- ○ c) 23 in.

3.
What comes next? _____
- ○ a)
- ○ b)
- ○ c)

4.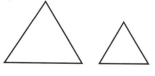
- ○ a) congruent
- ○ b) not congruent
- ○ c) symmetrical

5. [star]
- ○ a) congruent
- ○ b) not congruent
- ○ c) symmetrical

6.
- ○ a) $\frac{3}{8}$
- ○ b) $\frac{2}{8}$
- ○ c) $\frac{3}{7}$

7. [triangle]
- ○ a) $\frac{2}{3}$
- ○ b) $\frac{1}{3}$
- ○ c) $\frac{1}{2}$

8.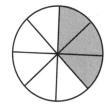
- ○ a) $\frac{1}{4}$
- ○ b) $\frac{2}{3}$
- ○ c) $\frac{1}{3}$

9.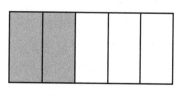
- ○ a) $\frac{5}{2}$
- ○ b) $\frac{1}{5}$
- ○ c) $\frac{2}{5}$

10.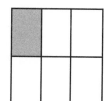
- ○ a) $\frac{1}{4}$
- ○ b) $\frac{1}{6}$
- ○ c) $\frac{1}{7}$

11.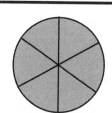
- ○ a) $\frac{6}{6}$
- ○ b) $\frac{5}{6}$
- ○ c) $\frac{1}{2}$

Unit 7

Name_____ Date_____

Fill in the circle next to the correct answer.

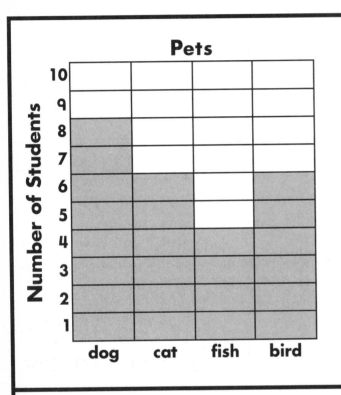

Pets

1. How many more students have cats than fish?
  - ○ a) 1
  - ○ b) 2
  - ○ c) 3

2. How many dogs and cats are there combined?
  - ○ a) 14
  - ○ b) 16
  - ○ c) 18

3. How many students have a pet?
  - ○ a) 22
  - ○ b) 23
  - ○ c) 24

4. How many students have birthdays in May?
  - ○ a) 3
  - ○ b) 4
  - ○ c) 5

5. How many students have birthdays in July and August combined?
  - ○ a) 8
  - ○ b) 9
  - ○ c) 10

6. Which month has the most birthdays?
  - ○ a) April
  - ○ b) May
  - ○ c) August

Birthdays

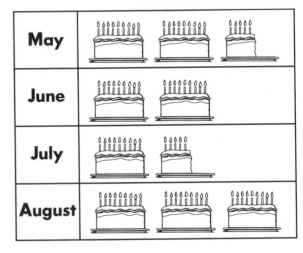

= 2 students

Fill in the circle next to the correct answer.

1. ○ a) 41¢ ○ b) 45¢ ○ c) 50¢	**2.** ○ a) 61¢ ○ b) 62¢ ○ c) 70¢
3. ○ a) 20¢ ○ b) 25¢ ○ c) 30¢	**4.** ○ a) 60¢ ○ b) 65¢ ○ c) 75¢
5. ○ a) 75¢ ○ b) 85¢ ○ c) 95¢	**6.** ○ a) 83¢ ○ b) 84¢ ○ c) 85¢
7. ○ a) 52¢ ○ b) 53¢ ○ c) 54¢	**8.** ○ a) 32¢ ○ b) 34¢ ○ c) 44¢

9. Karen has $9.20. The movie she wants to buy costs $9.99. How much more money does Karen need?

○ a) 69¢
○ b) 79¢
○ c) 89¢

10. Ray has 60¢. Joe has 15¢. Bob has 20¢. How much money do they have altogether?

○ a) 85¢
○ b) 95¢
○ c) 99¢

Practice Test: Time

Name_____ Date_____

Fill in the circle next to the correct answer.

1.
○ a) 3:55
○ b) 4:00
○ c) 10:20

2.
○ a) 9:00
○ b) 9:05
○ c) 9:10

3.
○ a) 12:30
○ b) 2:15
○ c) 1:15

4.
○ a) 5:00
○ b) 9:20
○ c) 11:25

5.
○ a) 1:40
○ b) 2:40
○ c) 3:40

6.
○ a) 4:45
○ b) 5:30
○ c) 6:30

7.
6 o'clock
○ a) 6:00
○ b) 7:00
○ c) 8:00

8.
three-thirty
○ a) 8:30
○ b) 3:30
○ c) 9:00

9. It is now 2 o'clock. In 2 hours and 30 minutes it will be _____.
○ a) 3:15
○ b) 3:30
○ c) 4:30

10. Eddie has soccer practice at 6:00. If the practice lasts 1 hour and 15 minutes, what time will it be over?
○ a) 7:15
○ b) 6:15
○ c) 8:00

Practice Test: Measurement

Name_____ Date_____

Fill in the circle next to the correct answer.

MARCH

S	M	T	W	T	F	S
1	2	3	4	5	6	7
8	9	10	11	12	13	14
15	16	17	18	19	20	21
22	23	24	25	26	27	28
29	30	31				

1. How many Mondays are in March?

   ○ a) 3
   ○ b) 4
   ○ c) 5

2. How many days are in March?

   ○ a) 31
   ○ b) 30
   ○ c) 29

3. A car weighs more than 1 kg.

   ○ a) false
   ○ b) true

4. A liter is used to measure _____.

   ○ a) length
   ○ b) weight
   ○ c) volume

5. How long is the pen?

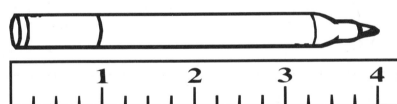

   ○ a) 4 inches
   ○ b) 6 inches
   ○ c) 8 inches

6. How long is the crayon?

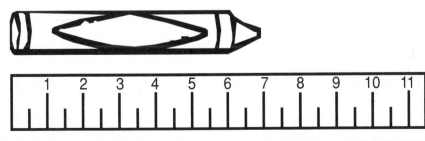

   ○ a) 8 centimeters
   ○ b) 9 centimeters
   ○ c) 7 centimeters

Unit 7

Practice Test: Multiplication

Name_____ Date_____

Fill in the circle next to the correct answer.

1.

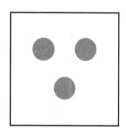

4 groups of 2 =

○a) 4
○b) 6
○c) 8

2.

2 groups of 3 =

○a) 4
○b) 6
○c) 8

3.
```
    7
  x 1
  ___
```
○a) 1
○b) 6
○c) 7

4.
```
    9
  x 0
  ___
```
○a) 0
○b) 8
○c) 9

5.
```
   45
  x 0
  ___
```
○a) 46
○b) 45
○c) 0

6.
```
   80
  x 1
  ___
```
○a) 80
○b) 81
○c) 82

7.
```
    2
  x 5
  ___
```
○a) 3
○b) 7
○c) 10

8.
```
    3
  x 3
  ___
```
○a) 6
○b) 9
○c) 1

Answer Key

Page 3
1. 17, 11, 18, 14, 12
2. 15, 13, 14, 16, 9
3. 9, 15, 11, 9, 10
4. 10, 12, 16, 14, 11

Page 4
1. 7, 8, 5, 2, 8
2. 6, 7, 9, 4, 5
3. 9, 2, 5, 3, 6

Page 5
1. 3, 6, 9, 9, 4
2. 8, 4, 9, 3, 8
3. 8, 5, 7, 7, 9
4. 6, 6, 8, 8, 5

Page 6
1. 8, 4, 8, 5, 9
2. 6, 8, 9, 3, 7
3. 6, 7, 4, 9, 6

Page 7
1. b	2. a	3. c
4. c	5. b	6. a
7. c	8. b	9. c
10. a	11. b	12. a
13. b	14. a	15. b

Page 8
1. 3	2. 7	3. 4
4. 9	5. 2	6. 8
7. 5	8. 1	9. 8

Page 9
1. +, −, −
2. −, +, −
3. +, −, −
4. −, +, −
5. +, −, −
6. +, −, +
7. −, −, +
8. +, +, −
9. +, −, +

Page 10
1. 39, 58, 83, 75, 77
2. 49, 28, 71, 55, 69
3. 48, 98, 84, 38, 86
4. 73, 92, 68, 87, 74

Page 11.
1. 37, 23, 30, 24, 17
2. 11, 31, 12, 22, 21
3. 25, 40, 13, 16, 46
4. 53, 44, 47, 15, 13

Page 12
1. 42	2. 31	3. 20
4. 11	5. 62	6. 35
7. 12	8. 76	9. 17
10. 54	11. 44	12. 23

Page 13
1. c	2. a	3. c
4. b	5. a	6. b
7. c	8. a	9. b
10. b	11. a	12. b
13. c	14. b	15. a

Page 14
1. 12 + 17 = 29
2. 26 + 11 = 37
3. 45 + 32 = 77
4. 50 + 18 = 68
5. 16 + 10 = 26
6. 34 + 24 = 58

Page 15
1. 21 − 11 = 13
2. 56 − 25 = 31
3. 49 − 21 = 28
4. 88 − 42 = 46
5. 27 − 16 = 11
6. 77 − 54 = 23

Page 16
1. 89 − 26 = 63
2. 42 + 36 = 78
3. 95 − 45 = 50
4. 53 − 12 = 41
5. 61 + 38 = 99
6. 24 + 13 = 37

Page 17
1. 90, 67, 98, 86, 36
2. 66, 99, 55, 77, 43
3. 87, 76, 49, 58, 90
4. 39, 68, 59, 88, 74

Page 18

Page 19
1. 55, 62, 83, 88, 70
2. 90, 95, 83, 90, 89

Page 20
1. 53, 44, 63, 81, 62
2. 88, 65, 60, 71, 89
3. 84, 75, 38, 83, 56
4. 62, 48, 80, 40, 58
5. 78, 69, 57, 50, 85

Page 21
1. ⟨17,⟩ 23, ⟨18,⟩ ⟨39,⟩ 26

2. ⟨14,⟩ ⟨5,⟩ 50, ⟨36,⟩ ⟨59⟩

Page 22
1. 35	2. 28	3. 19	4. 46
5. 35	6. 49	7. 29	8. 18
9. 6	10. 20	11. 17	12. 28
13. 49	14. 46	15. 8	16. 36

Page 23
1. b	2. c	3. a
4. c	5. b	6. b
7. b	8. a	9. c
10. a	11. c	12. a
13. c	14. b	15. b

Page 24
1. 15 + 18 = 33
2. 46 + 29 = 75
3. 14 + 7 = 21
4. 23 + 17 = 40
5. 28 + 28 = 56
6. 33 + 29 = 62

Page 25
1. 14 + 16 = 30
2. 42 + 29 = 71
3. 75 + 19 = 94
4. 27 + 18 = 45
5. 13 + 9 = 22
6. 29 + 39 = 68

Page 26
1. 35 – 16 = 19
2. 41 – 28 = 13
3. 74 – 49 = 25
4. 67 – 29 = 38
5. 83 – 37 = 46
6. 52 – 18 = 34

Page 27
1. 33 – 18 = 15
2. 91 – 67 = 24
3. 44 – 26 = 18
4. 60 – 25 = 35
5. 58 – 29 = 29
6. 22 – 8 = 14

Page 28
1. 27 + 35 = 62
2. 53 – 36 = 17
3. 85 – 57 = 28
4. 61 + 19 = 80
5. 42 + 29 = 71
6. 72 – 38 = 34

Page 29
1. 2 (100's), 4 (10's), 3 (1's) = 243
2. 1 (100's), 8 (10's), 7 (1's) = 187
3. 5 (100's), 1 (10's), 6 (1's) = 516
4. 4 (100's), 6 (10's), 1 (1's) = 461
5. 3 (100's), 3 (10's), 3 (1's) = 333
6. 3 (100's), 2 (10's), 9 (1's) = 329

Page 30
1. 365	2. 852
3. 746	4. 923
5. 444	6. 111
7. 614	8. 539
9. 278	10. 593

Page 31
1. 342, 931
2. 567, 474
3. 219, 643
4. 196, 826
5. 785, 123
6. 100 + 40 + 9, 200 + 60 + 7
7. 500 + 30 + 2, 400 + 50 + 1
8. 700 + 20 + 8, 900 + 80 + 6
9. 300 + 10 + 4, 600 + 90 + 8
10. 800 + 70 + 3, 500 + 50 + 5

Page 32
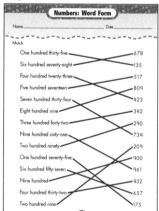

Page 33

Page 34
1. 796, 858, 969
2. 779, 966, 983
3. 888, 894, 858
4. 537, 615, 392

Page 35
1. 697 2. 59   3. 864   4. 875
5. 474 6. 916 7. 327   8. 749
9. 222 10. 660 11. 438 12. 987
13. 710 14. 562 15. 234 16. 399

Page 36
Pattern: The sums increase by 25.

1. (600,) 389, (625,) 589, 489
2. (650,) (675,) 497, 499, 496
3. 559, (700,) (725,) 444, (750)
4. 588, 598, (775,) (800,) 599
5. (825,) 443, (850,) (875,) (900)

Page 37
1. 909, 678, 988, 865, 366
2. 776, 999, 553, 876, 432
3. 870, 764, 491, 589, 906
4. 394, 685, 593, 887, 745

Page 38
1. (715,) (594,) 589
2. (744,) 456, (842)
3. (949,) (617,) 398

Page 39
1. 483, 376, 618, 816, 622
2. 888, 653, 550, 719, 890
3. 947, 760, 387, 834, 569
4. 624, 408, 808, 409, 587
5. 789, 695, 576, 293, 851

Page 40

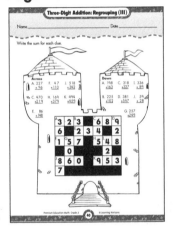

Page 41
1. 623, 304, 458
2. 332, 316, 741
3. 247, 300, 322

Page 42
1. 401   2. 311   3. 525   4. 642
5. 350   6. 712   7. 745   8. 286
9. 839   10. 123 11. 444 12. 607
13. 254 14. 563 15. 802 16. 176

Page 43
1. 223, 100, 354, 550, 467
2. 642, 136, 301, 230, 120
3. 302, 488, 611, 542, 313
4. 662, 140, 275, 412, 507
5. 388, 731, 216, 460, 459

Page 44

Subtract.				
1. 549 −134 **415** −204 **211** −101 **110**	2. 677 −225 **452** −251 **201** −101 **100**	3. 289 −131 **158** −126 **32** − 30 **2**	4. 488 −123 **365** −105 **260** −230 **30**	5. 976 −412 **564** −312 **252** − 41 **211**
6. 888 −241 **647** −213 **434** −122 **312** −211 **101**	7. 796 −313 **483** −140 **343** −211 **132** −112 **20**	8. 999 −452 **547** −100 **447** − 321 **126** −101 **25**	9. 574 −120 **454** −150 **304** −102 **202** −100 **102**	10. 697 − 13 **684** − 31 **653** − 310 **343** −130 **213**

Page 45
1. (352,) (406,) 113
2. (494,) 150, (519)
3. 625, (238,) (742)

Page 46
1. 114, 330, 193, 240, 415
2. 317, 180, 489, 349, 651
3. 522, 781, 503, 223, 90
4. 345, 377, 645, 247, 519
5. 838, 452, 236, 213, 499

Page 47
1. 151, 326, 254, 470
2. 648, 307, 593, 200
3. 275, 207, 82, 619
4. 150, 458, 96, 501

B	I	N	G	O
151				
	470			
		501		
			648	
				96

Page 48
1. b	2. a	3. c
4. c	5. c	6. a
7. b	8. a	9. c
10. c	11. b	12. a
13. a	14. c	15. b

Page 49
1. a	2. c	3. b
4. c	5. b	6. a
7. b	8. a	9. c
10. b	11. a	12. c
13. a	14. c	15. b

Page 50
1. 132 + 257 = 389
2. 268 + 527 = 795
3. 375 + 297 = 672
4. 328 + 480 = 808
5. 249 + 518 = 767
6. 125 + 87 = 212

Page 51
1. 509 + 187 = 696
2. 89 + 89 = 178
3. 325 + 129 = 454
4. 670 + 89 = 759
5. 449 + 449 = 898
6. 129 + 187 = 316
7. John
8. Trevor

Page 52
1. 410 − 387 = 23
2. 912 − 797 = 115
3. 564 − 181 = 383
4. 953 − 459 = 494
5. 800 − 282 = 518
6. 175 − 38 = 137

Page 53
1. 612 − 386 = 226
2. 612 − 475 = 137
3. 275 − 158 = 117
4. 502 − 419 = 83
5. 385 − 150 = 235
6. 123 − 81 = 42

Page 54
1. 380 − 237 = 143
2. 110 + 97 = 207
3. 441 + 129 = 570
4. 748 − 465 = 283
5. 584 − 137 = 447
6. 114 + 247 = 361

Page 55

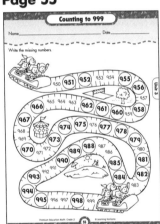

Page 56
1. 157, 423, 235
2. 287, 195, 607
3. 121, 169, 173
4. 547, 231, 189
5. 810, 522, 436
6. 198, 676, 420
7. 222, 950, 678
8. 624, 508
9. 12
10. 11

Page 57
1. 376	2. 889
3. 161	4. 224
5. 490	6. 605
7. 972	8. 793

Page 58
1. 680, 424, 919
2. 513, 330, 790
3. 801, 185, 223
4. 999, 438, 526
5. 200, 750, 102
6. 335, 657, 800

Page 59
1. 270, 415
2. 552, 669
3. 884, 941
4. 313, 526
5. 747, 400
6. 178, 290

Page 60
1. 312, 231, 123
2. 743, 634, 467
3. 349, 214, 190
4. 528, 497, 479
5. 821, 804, 757
6. 321, 320, 312
7. 900, 880, 816
8. 617, 600, 599
9. 931, 930, 929
10. 111, 110, 101
11. 576, 557, 457

Answer Key

Page 61

1. 457, 475, 476
2. 588, 590, 600
3. 355, 368, 427
4. 788, 878, 897
5. 112, 121, 211
6. 989, 990, 999
7. 463, 634, 643
8. 757, 775, 777
9. 246, 264, 426
10. 598, 600, 659
11. 303, 323, 333

Page 62

1. 134 < 150
2. 396 > 325
3. 232 < 254
4. 325 = 325
5. 124 > 100
6. 703 < 705
7. 228 > 222
8. 373 > 334
9. 101 > 81
10. 511 > 500
11. 324 = 324
12. 601 > 300

Page 63

1. third
2. sixth
3. eleventh
4. seventh
5. eighth
6. second
7. fourth
8. first

Page 64

1. 773, 774, 776, 777
2. 582, 583, 585, 586, 587
3. 991, 992, 994, 995, 996
4. 454, 137, 700
5. 309, 430, 749
6. <, =, >   7. >, <, >
8. 988   9. 301

Page 65

1. 30, 40, 50, 60
2. 10, 20, 30, 50
3. 30, 50, 60
4. 50, 70, 80
5. 50, 70, 90, 100

Page 66

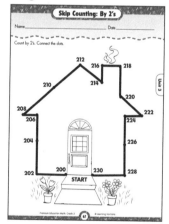

Page 67

Page 68

1. 12, 2. 21 , 3. 15, 4. 24, 5. 30

Page 69

1. 65, 70, 75, 85
   Rule: skip counting by 5
2. 12, 15, 18, 21
   Rule: skip counting by 3
3. 70, 74, 78, 82
   Rule: skip counting by 2
4. 80, 110, 130, 140
   Rule: skip counting by 10

Page 70

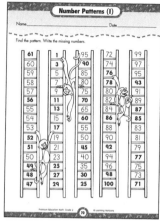

Page 71

Page 72

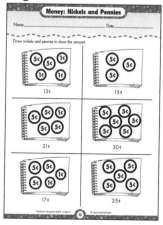

Answer Key

Page 73
1. 10¢ + 7¢ = 17¢
2. 20¢ + 4¢ = 24¢
3. 40¢ + 2¢ = 42¢
4. 30¢ + 3¢ = 33¢
5. 50¢ + 1¢ = 51¢

Page 74
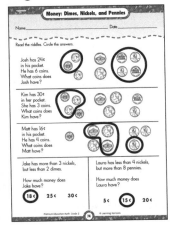

Page 75
1. 25¢ (color purse)
2. 25¢ (color purse)
3. 18¢
4. 24¢
5. 21¢
6. 25¢ (color purse)
7. 25¢ (color purse)
8. 20¢

Page 76
1. 25¢, 35¢, 45¢, 50¢, 51¢, 52¢, 52¢
2. 25¢, 35¢, 45¢, 55¢, 65¢, 75¢, 75¢
3. 25¢, 35¢, 45¢, 50¢, 55¢, 56¢, 56¢
4. 25¢, 35¢, 40¢, 41¢, 42¢, 43¢, 43¢
5. 25¢, 50¢, 55¢, 55¢

Page 77
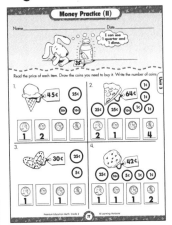

Page 78
1. F
2. B
3. A
4. G
5. I
6. E
7. J
8. C
9. D
10. H

Page 79
1. $3.05
2. $4.71
3. $4.20
4. $3.04

Page 80
1. c
2. c
3. b
4. a
5. b
6. a
7. c
8. b

Page 81
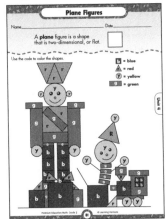

Page 82
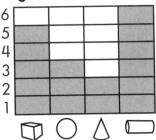

Page 83
1. 4, 4, 4
2. 3, 3, 3
3. 4, 4, 4
4. 8, 8, 8

Page 84
1. congruent
2. not congruent
3. congruent
4. congruent
5. congruent
6. not congruent
7. not congruent
8. congruent
9. congruent
10. not congruent
11. congruent
12. not congruent

Page 85

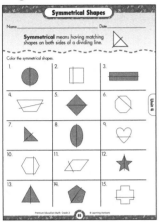

Page 86

1. 15 in.	2. 16 in.	3. 32 in.
4. 17 in.	5. 24 in.	6. 20 in.
7. 14 in.	8. 20 in.	9. 24 in.
10. 20 in.	11. 30 in.	12. 22 in.

Page 87

1.

2.

3.

4.

5.

6.

7.

Page 88

1. a	2. c
3. b	4. c
5. a	6. b
7. b	8. a
9. c	
10. b	

Page 89

1. math
2. science
3. 8
4. 12
5. 4
6. 20

Page 90

1. 22
2. 19
3. Mr. Clark's
4. Mrs. Smith's
5. 7
6. Answers will vary.

Page 91

1. 8
2. 36
3. 4
4. Allen
5. Ford
6. 6
7. 19
8. Allen
9. Ford
10. Allen

Page 92

1. (A,1)	2. (E, 4)	3. (B, 4)
4. (F, 2)	5. (C, 1)	6. (G, 4)
7. (D, 2)	8. (C, 3)	9. (G, 1)

Page 93

1. 6
2. 5
3. notebooks
4. crayons
5. 22

Page 94

1. 3		4. snake
2. 3		5. 24
3. 6		6. $\frac{1}{2}$

Page 95

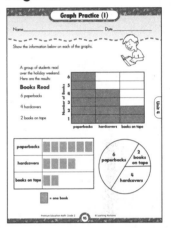

Page 96

Page 97

1. $\frac{5}{8}$	2. $\frac{1}{3}$	3. $\frac{4}{6}$
4. $\frac{1}{2}$	5. $\frac{3}{5}$	6. $\frac{2}{4}$
7. $\frac{6}{7}$	8. $\frac{1}{4}$	9. $\frac{4}{8}$

Answer Key

Page 98

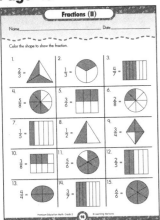

Page 99

1. >   2. =
3. <   4. >
5. =   6. <
7. $\frac{1}{6}$, $\frac{1}{4}$, $\frac{1}{2}$, $\frac{2}{3}$, $\frac{6}{8}$,

Page 100

1. $\frac{2}{3}$, $\frac{5}{6}$, $\frac{1}{4}$

2. $\frac{6}{8}$, $\frac{3}{3}$, $\frac{1}{2}$

3.

4.

5. >   6. <

Page 101

1. 9:00, 2:00, 3:00
2. 11:00, 4:00, 7:00
3. 5, 12, 10
4. 8, 6, 1

Page 102

1. 7:30, 2:30, 4:30
2. 8:30, 1:30, 6:30
3. 12:30, 5:30, 10:30
4. 3:30, 11:30, 9:30

Page 103

1. 10:30, 1:00, 12:30
2. 7:00, 6:30, 3:30
3. 2:00, 5:00, 4:30
4. nine-thirty, 11 o'clock, eight-thirty

Page 104

1. 15, 8, 8:15
2. 30, 10, 10:30
3. 15, 2, 2:15
4. 45, 1, 1:45

Page 105

1. 8:30, 1:15, 5:45
2. 11:45, 6:15, 2:30
3. 7:30, 8:45, 12:15

Page 106

1. 9:45, 2:15, 3:45
2. 11:15, 4:15, 7:45
3. 5:45, 12:15, 10:45
4. 8:15, 6:15, 1:45

Page 107

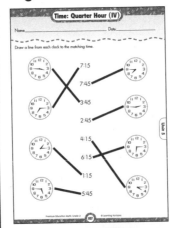

Page 108

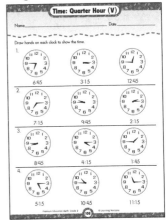

Page 109

05, 10, (15) (20) (25) 30,
(35) (40) (45) (50) (55) 60

Page 110

1. 1:10   2. 3:40
3. 9:35   4. 2:05
5. 7:20   6. 10:55
7. 6:50   8. 8:25

Page 111

1. 10:20, 7:05, 4:25
2. 2:35, 1:50, 6:10
3. 5:40, 8:15, 2:30
4. 3:55, 11:05, 9:45

Page 112

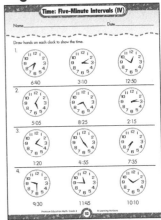

Page 113

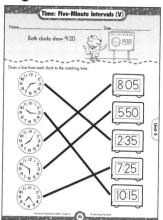

Page 114

1. a.m.   5. p.m.
2. p.m.   6. a.m.
3. a.m.   7. p.m.
4. p.m.

Page 115

Answers will vary.

Page 116

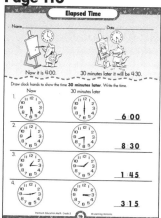

Page 117

1. 9:30   4. 2:45
2. 10:45   5. 3:35
3. 4:00

Page 118

1. b   2. c
3. a   4. b
5. a   6. c
7. a   8. c

Page 119

1. November
2. 30
3. Thursday
4. four
5. seven
6. Thursday
7. November 10
8. November 19
9. Tuesday
10. December

Page 120

1. 14 cm.   5. 8 in.
2. 4 cm.   6. 5 in.
3. 10 cm.   7. 5 in.
4. 3 cm.

Page 121

1. b   2. a   3. b
4. a   5. b   6. b
7. b   8. a   9. a

Page 122

1. b   2. a   3. b
4. a   5. a   6. a
7. b   8. a   9. b

Page 123

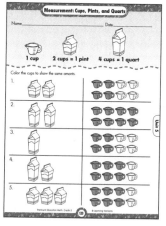

Page 124

1. a   2. a   3. b
4. a   5. b   6. a
7. a   8. b   9. b

Page 125

1. 60°, 20°, 0°, 50°
2. 40°, -10°, 80°, 30°
3. 10°, 70°, 30°, 60°

Page 126

1. 4 in.
2. 9 cm.
3. 4 cups
4. b
5. a

Page 127

1. d   5. g
2. f   6. b
3. a   7. e
4. h   8. c

Page 128

1. 3 × 4 = 12
2. 2 × 6 = 12
3. 4 × 5 = 20
4. 4 × 4 = 16

Page 129
1. 8   2. 9
3. 12   4. 10
5. 18   6. 20

Page 130
1. 6, 6
2. 16, 16
3. 10, 10
4. 9, 9
5. 12, 12

Page 131
1. 2 + 2 = 4
2. 1 + 1 + 1 + 1 = 4
3. 3 + 3 + 3 + 3 = 12
4. 5 = 5
5. 1 + 1 + 1 + 1 + 1 + 1 = 6
6. 5 + 5 + 5 = 15
7. 2 + 2 + 2 + 2 = 8
8. 3 = 3

Page 132
1. 0, 0, 0, 0, 0
2. 0, 0, 0, 0, 0
3. 0, 0, 0, 0, 0
4. 0, 0, 0, 0, 0

Page 133
1. 8, 5, 6, 3, 7
2. 9, 2, 4, 7, 2
3. 46, 28, 44, 68, 73
4. 29, 33, 55, 99, 82

Page 134
1. 2, 5, 2 × 5 = 10
2. 2, 4, 2 × 4 = 8
3. 2, 6, 2 × 6 = 12
4. 2, 2, 2 × 2 = 4
5. 2, 7, 2 × 7 = 14
6. 2, 8, 2 × 8 = 16

Page 135
1. 3, 5, 3 × 5 = 15
2. 3, 4, 3 × 4 = 12
3. 3, 6, 3 × 6 = 18
4. 3, 2, 3 × 2 = 6
5. 3, 7, 3 × 7 = 21
6. 3, 8, 3 × 8 = 24

Page 136
1. 9   4. 6
2. 3   5. 3
3. 4

Page 137
1. 6   4. 13
2. 12   5. 18
3. 15   6. 8

Page 138
1. 8   4. 6
2. 4   5. 3
3. 5

Page 139
1. b   2. c   3. a   4. b
5. a   6. c   7. b   8. a
9. c   10. b   11. a   12. b

Page 140
1. c   2. a   3. b   4. b
5. a   6. c   7. b   8. a
9. c   10. b   11. a   12. b

Page 141
1. b   2. c   3. a   4. c
5. c   6. a   7. b   8. b
9. a   10. a   11. a   12. b

Page 142
1. c   2. a   3. b   4. a
5. c   6. b   7. a   8. c
9. b   10. a   11. c   12. b

Page 143
1. a   2. c   3. b   4. a
5. c   6. a   7. b   8. b
9. c   10. a   11. a   12. b

Page 144
1. b   4. b
2. a   5. c
3. c   6. a

Page 145
1. c   2. b   3. a   4. b
5. c   6. a   7. b   8. b
9. c   10. b   11. a

Page 146
1. b   4. c
2. a   5. b
3. c   6. c

Page 147
1. a   2. b   3. c   4. b
5. c   6. a   7. b   8. c
9. b   10. b

Page 148
1. a   2. b   3. c   4. c
5. b   6. a   7. a   8. b
9. c   10. a

Page 149
1. c   4. c
2. a   5. a
3. b   6. c

Page 150
1. c   2. b
3. c   4. a
5. c   6. a
7. c   8. b